The Wonderful Worlds
of
WALT DISNEY

STORIES FROM
OTHER LANDS

Photographs and Illustrations
by The Walt Disney Studio

GOLDEN PRESS · NEW YORK

The text for the chapters adapted from the *People and Places* film series is based on the film narration by: Dwight Hauser; Otto Englander; Winston Hibler; Ted Sears; Alan Jaggs; Francis Cockrell; Ralph Wright; Harrison Negley; James Algar; Trudy Knapp; Cecil Maiden

The photographs in this book were taken by: Ernst A. Heiniger; Herbert Knapp; Amleto Fattori, *Filmeco, Rome, Italy;* Raymond Bricon; Rickard Tegstrom; John Hardman; Kenneth Talbot; Betty O'Connor; Joe O'Connor; James R. Simon; Hugh A. Wilmar; Lloyd Beebe; Jane Werner Watson; Johnson Motor Co., *Waukegan, Illinois;* Photo Researchers, Inc., Jean and Tom Hollyman, Ed Drews; Robert J. Bezucha

The paintings in the *People and Places* series are by: Art Riley; Joshua Meador; and Joseph Cellini

CONTENTS

WALT DISNEY'S
MARY POPPINS

AN EAST wind was blowing over Cherry Tree Lane, where Jane and Michael Banks lived with their parents, Mr. and Mrs. Banks. Besides there was Katie Nanna, the nursemaid, who doesn't really count because at the time the east wind blew she was leaving Number Seventeen.

The wind was whipping gustily through the leaves as Katie Nanna came stamping down the stairs with her bags, hopped into the waiting hansom cab and rode away, leaving Jane and Michael Banks without a nanny.

Mr. Banks was a very busy man. He never had time for any fun, but he *did* know his duty to wife and family. He wrote an advertisement to the *Times*. And the next morning a line of applicants stretched down the Banks' front walk all the way to the Lane.

Jane and Michael looked down from the nursery window. "They're horrible!" said Michael with a shudder. But as the children watched, the east wind started up again,

blowing through the branches of the cherry trees in the Lane. And it tweaked at their hats and snatched at their umbrellas and blew all those would-be nannies away! Yes, over the fence posts, over the tree tops, quite out of sight they flew!

Then down over the park, swinging gently back and forth as she held to the handle of her umbrella, a marvelous person came floating on the wind. "It's she!" gasped Jane at the nursery window. "She's just the one we wanted." And as they watched, the person floated down to the front porch, put down her carpet bag, closed her umbrella, and rang the front door bell. That was how Mary Poppins came to Jane and Michael Banks on the east wind.

While Jane and Michael watched in astonishment from the nursery landing, Mary Poppins slid gracefully up the banister and set down her carpet bag. The children could see that it was empty. But from the empty carpet bag she took one hat rack, one large, gilt-edged mirror, a rubber plant and a lighted floor lamp!

"There!" she said, looking around the room. "That's a bit more comfortable, I would say!"

"Now," said Mary Poppins with a look around the nursery, "it's time for a game called Tidy up the Nursery."

"I don't like the sound of it," said Michael. But Mary Poppins only smiled.

"In every job that must be done," she said, "we find an element of fun. We find the fun and *snap!* the job's a game!"

And when Mary Poppins snapped her fingers, all Jane's dolls settled themselves neatly on the nursery shelves. Michael's soldiers, made of lead, marched to tents beneath the bed. Toys and clowns and wood blocks flew into their magic box. Shirts and skirts and waistcoats, too, soared to closets out of view. In no time at all, the nursery was tidy. "That's better," Mary Poppins sniffed. "Now it looks less like a bear pit."

"Let's do it again," said Michael.

"Nonsense," said Mary Poppins. "It is time for an outing in the park. Come along," she said. "Spit-spot!"

In the park they met Bert, the jack-of-all-trades. He was down on his knees drawing pictures in colored chalks on the sidewalk. Jane and Michael stooped down to look at each picture.

"Oh here's a lovely one," sighed Jane. "I wish we could go there."

"A typical English countryside," Bert pointed out with pardonable pride. "Quite a suitable spot for travel and high adventure. Why not? And down the road there's a country fair. Come along." And taking each child by a hand he winked at them. "Bit of magic," he explained. "It's easy. You wink. . . . You think. . . . You do a double blink. . . . You close your eyes and—jump!"

With a sniff Mary Poppins put up her umbrella, and away they all floated straight into the drawing of the English countryside.

It was a beautiful spot, green and quiet and sparkling with sun.

"Mary Poppins," said Bert, "you look beautiful!" And so she did, for suddenly she was dressed in the height of fashion, from the wide curly brim of her hat to the diamond buttons on her shoes.

"You look fine too, Bert," said Mary Poppins. And so he did, in a new suit of clothes and a new straw hat.

"I thought you said there was a fair," said Michael, who was not impressed by clothes, though he looked very fine himself.

"So I did," said Bert. "Just down the road and over the hill."

Bert gave Mary Poppins his arm, and off they all strolled through the countryside. All the birds and animals came out to greet Mary—the lambs and the cows and the old gray horse, the geese and the turtles in the pond. The whole world seemed to dance for joy, and along with Bert the animals sang, "Any day with Mary is a jolly holiday."

In a sunny spot among the trees they found a tea pavilion, where they stopped for a lovely afternoon tea. The waiters looked exactly like penguins.

When their tea was finished, they waltzed away, down the road and over the hill to the merry-go-round. It slowed down just as they approached it, and they leaped aboard. Each one landed gracefully in the saddle of a wooden horse.

"Imagine!" said Jane. "Our own private merry-go-round."

"It's very nice," said Bert, putting on airs, "very nice indeed, if you don't want to go anywhere."

"Who says we are not going anywhere?" said Mary Poppins with a toss of her head. And she had a quiet word with the guard.

"Right-o, Mary Poppins," smiled the guard, and he lifted his cap. Then he pulled the tallest lever on the merry-go-round machine—and away went their horses *tum-tum-tee-tum* across the countryside.

From the distance came the sound of a hunting horn. "Follow me!" called Mary Poppins over her shoulder. And away they rode to the sound of the horn, passing the huntsmen one and all. They even started to pass the fox, until Bert scooped him up and gave him a ride.

Jane and Michael were riding so hard and fast that at first they did not notice that Mary Poppins had left their side. Then, "It's a race!" cried Michael. "And look, Bert!" cried Jane. "Mary Poppins is winning!" "So she is!" said Bert.

There came the leaders, pounding down the track. And as Jane and Michael watched, the riders pulled aside, letting Mary Poppins ride between them straight to the finish line.

Jane and Michael were sitting on the fence with Bert, eating taffy apples, when the first big round raindrops fell. Then came a flash of lightning, and the rain came pouring down!

"Michael! Jane! Don't run about. Stay close to me," called Mary Poppins. As they huddled close together under her umbrella, all the countryside around them seemed to melt away. . . . They were back in the park! And on the pavement at their feet Bert's drawings were melting into bright puddles of rain.

"Spit-spot," said Mary Poppins. "Hurry along, children, or we'll be late for tea. Good-bye, Bert." And soon they were snug

in the nursery with a fire glowing in the
fireplace.

On the hearth stood Jane's and Michael's
shoes, drying out from their day in the rain.
Beside them leaned Mary Poppins' umbrella.
Tea was over and Mary Poppins was tucking
Jane and Michael into bed.

"Mary Poppins, you won't ever leave us,
will you?" Jane said sleepily. "Will you
stay," begged Michael, "if we promise to be
good?" "That's a pie-crust promise," said
Mary Poppins. "Easily made, easily broken. I
shall stay until the wind changes." And that
was all that she would say.

The next thing Jane and Michael knew,
Mary Poppins was opening the curtains.
"Up, up!" she ordered. "No dawdling. It's a
glorious day—super-cali-fragil-istic, I might

say. We're going for a walk. Spit-spot. This
way."

"Super-cali-fragil-istic," sang Jane and
Michael as they danced along the walk. They
almost bumped into Mary Poppins when she
stopped to speak to a little dog. The children had never seen the dog before, but
Mary Poppins seemed to know him well. She
called him Andrew. The little dog barked
noisily at Mary Poppins. "Again?" said Mary
Poppins. "I'll go straight away."

Taking Jane and Michael by the hand,
Mary Poppins started off the way Andrew
had come. And in no more than a moment
or two she was rapping at the door of a
small, quaint house.

It was Bert who opened the door. "How is
he?" Mary Poppins asked. "Never seen him

like this," said Bert soberly, "and that's the truth." He pushed the door wide open. Jane and Michael peeked in.

A large, cheerful room lay before them. In the center stood a table laid for tea. "Bless—bless my soul," said a voice rich with chuckles. "Is that Mary Poppins? I'm delighted to see you."

The voice came from above. They looked up, and there in the air sat Mary Poppins' Uncle Albert, chuckling merrily.

"You have just got to stop laughing, Uncle Albert," said Mary Poppins sternly. "I know my dear, but I do enjoy it so," said Uncle Albert. Here the chuckles bubbled out so that he bobbed against the ceiling. "And the moment I start laughing—hee hee—it's all *up* with me."

He looked so comic that Jane and Michael, though they were trying hard to be polite, just couldn't help doing what they did. They began to chuckle.

By now Bert was rolling about, shaking with laughter. Soon he rose from the floor and was bobbing about beside Uncle Albert. At the sight of him, Jane and Michael found themselves simply filled with laughter, too. They grew lighter and lighter until their heads bumped the ceiling! Only Mary Poppins remained firmly on the ground.

"You're the silliest things I've ever seen," said Mary Poppins severely from below, "or my name isn't Mary Poppins."

"Speaking of names," said Bert, "I know a man with a wooden leg named Smith . . ."

"Really?" chuckled Uncle Albert. "What's

the name of his other leg?" And they all roared with laughter, bouncing in the air.

"Now then, Jane, Michael! It's time for tea," said Mary Poppins.

"Won't you pour out, Mary Poppins?" asked Uncle Albert.

At that the tea table came soaring through the air and Mary Poppins rose sedately to sit near the tea pot.

"I'm having such a good time, my dear," said Uncle Albert as they laughed their way through tea. "I wish you could all stay up here with me always."

"We'll jolly well have to," grinned Michael. "There's no way to get down."

"Well, to be honest," said Uncle Albert, "there *is* a way. Think of something sad and down you go."

"Time to go home." Mary Poppins' voice sounded like a trumpet above all the laughter in the room.

And at that saddest thought of all, down they all came with a bump.

Back home, Jane and Michael tried to tell Mr. Banks about the wonderful tea party and the laughing and the man with the wooden leg named Smith. But he did not seem to understand.

"Poppins," he said severely, "I'm disappointed in you. I am disturbed to hear my children speak about popping in and out of chalk pavement-drawings. Fox hunts, race tracks, tea parties on the ceiling—highly questionable outings. Words like super-cali-fra-craj-uh—"

"Super-cali-fragil-istic," said Mary Poppins.

"Of course. Thank you," said Mr. Banks. "Now if they must go on outings, they should have a purpose. They must learn of solid things, like banking. . . ."

"I understand," said Mary Poppins. "Tomorrow, freshly pressed and neatly dressed, Jane and Michael will be at your side."

"At my side?" cried Mr. Banks. "Where are we going?"

"To the bank, of course," said Mary Poppins. "Just as you proposed."

Jane and Michael could scarcely believe their ears. An outing with their father!

"Yes," said Mary Poppins, "and on the way to the bank you'll see the old bird lady on the steps of St. Paul's selling her bags of crumbs. 'Feed the birds, feed the birds, tuppence the bag,' she cries. And all around the cathedral, the Saints and Apostles look down, and they smile when someone shows he cares—with tuppence for a bag of crumbs."

Next morning, just as Mary Poppins had promised, Jane and Michael did see the old bird lady on the cathedral steps. "Feed the birds! Tuppence the bag," she cried.

"Please, father, may we feed the birds?" asked Jane.

"I've got tuppence from my money box," said Michael. "It's just as Mary Poppins says."

"I am not interested in what Mary Poppins says," said Mr. Banks. "When we get to

the bank, I shall show you what may be done with tuppence."

The bank was a great and awesome place. No one spoke above a whisper, so it seemed. Soon Michael and Jane were being presented to the Senior Mr. Dawes. He was a very, very old gentleman, gray and wrinkled and pinched and musty. He was the head of the bank.

"These are my children, Mr. Dawes," said Mr. Banks. "They wish to open an account."

"Oh, capital, capital!" said Mr. Dawes. "How much money have you, young man?"

"Tuppence," said Michael. "But I want it to feed the birds."

"Fiddlesticks," said Mr. Dawes. "Feed the birds and what have you got? Fat birds! But put your money in the bank, and safe and sound as the turn of a crank, your tuppence will draw interest and compound. You'll have railways, you'll have ships, river dams and ocean trips . . ." And he snatched Michael's tuppence from his hand.

"No!" said Michael. "I want to feed the birds. Give me back my tuppence!" And he snatched his tuppence back and ran.

"Michael! Jane!" shouted Mr. Banks angrily. But it was too late. The children had dashed out of the bank.

Jane and Michael ran up streets, down alleys, through the strange and busy ways of London Town.

As the children rounded a corner, not knowing where they were, a strange figure appeared before them, smudged with soot and bristling with brooms. It reached out both arms to them.

"Let us go!" cried Michael. "Let my sister alone."

"Easy now! Your old friend Bert isn't going to harm you."

And Bert it was, dressed as a chimney sweep. "Now," he asked, "who's after you?"

"Father is," said Jane. "He's furious."

"Now, now," said Bert. "There must be some mistake. Your father is a fine gentleman who loves you. He's the one you should feel sorry for, working in that cold, heartless bank all day."

"Oh, Bert," said Jane. "Do you think father needs our help?"

"I'll give him my tuppence," said Michael with a sigh.

It was late afternoon when Bert came home with Michael and Jane, into Cherry Tree Lane. They had had a fine frolic on the way with a whole band of chimney sweeps. Over the rooftops they had gone, and the sweeps were just dancing on their way when Mr. Banks came home.

"What's all this?" cried Mr. Banks as the sweeps danced past him.

"Oh, Father," said Jane. "I'm so glad you got home in time. Every one of those chimney sweeps shook your hand, so you're going to be very lucky."

"That may well be," said Mr. Banks. "I explained to the men at the bank, you see, about Mary Poppins and the bird woman, and Uncle Albert and the laughing, and the man with the wooden leg named Smith . . . and the whole super-cali-fragil-istic thing. And they all laughed. Even old Mr. Dawes laughed—it's the first time I've ever seen such a thing!"

Just then a brisk wind whipped around the corner. At Number Seventeen, Cherry Tree Lane, Mary Poppins stood at the window and sniffed at the breeze. In the street below she could see Mr. Banks, an arm around each child.

"I see the wind has changed," said Mary Poppins to herself. "It's time to go."

And as Mr. Banks and the children came up the front steps, Mary Poppins, properly dressed in her hat and coat, and carpet bag in hand, opened her umbrella. The wind slipped under it and away she flew—over the front gate, over the branches of the cherry trees in the lane.

"She's going, Jane," said Michael tearfully.

"Don't cry, children," said Mr. Banks. "She may be back. Let's give her a splendid send-off. Let's fly our kites!"

"You'll fly kites with us?" said Michael.

"By all means," said Mr. Banks happily.

And soon he and the children—and even Mrs. Banks—had kites flying high in the windy sky to wave Mary Poppins on her way.

WALT DISNEY'S THE SWORD IN THE STONE

ONCE IN old England there lived a nobleman who had two boys of whom he was very fond. Sir Ector was his name.

Kay, the elder boy, was of great size and strength of bone. He was also stubborn and lazy, but he was the nobleman's own son. When he grew older he would be Sir Kay and master of the castle.

The younger boy was called Wart. He was an adopted son, and could not hope to become a knight. Nevertheless the scrawny little fellow was full of smiles, and not one bit jealous of Kay.

One day Wart merrily followed Kay to a forest's edge. To keep out of the way there, Wart climbed a tree while Kay fitted a bow to an arrow and took aim at a deer. Kay aimed true, but just then there was a great cracking sound. It was the tree branch breaking under Wart's weight.

Startled, Kay released the arrow too quickly. It flew wide of the deer and disappeared into the forest. Watching it vanish, Kay shook with rage.

"Oh, please, Kay. I'm sorry," cried Wart. "I'll get it for you."

And he ran to search for the arrow in the forest, a dark and perilous place.

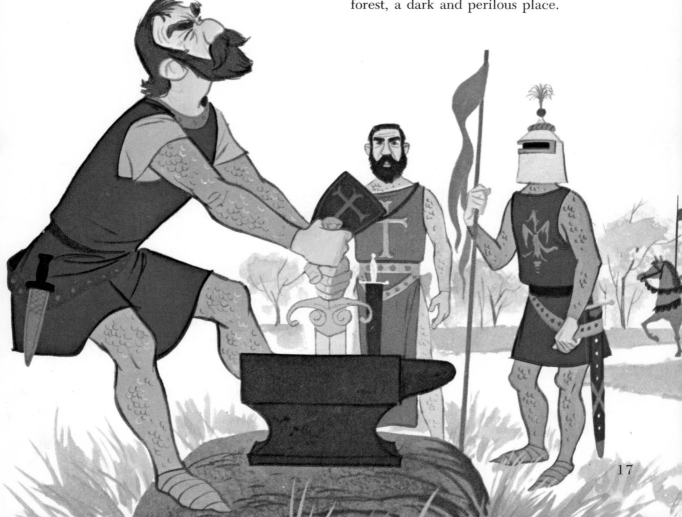

The perilous forest was no different from the rest of England in those days. Many years before, so long ago that Wart could not even remember it, good King Uther had ruled the land wisely and well. But when Uther died, he left no heir to the throne.

After Uther's death all the lords and nobles came to the greatest church in London Town to see if God would show them who should be king. There a wondrous thing happened. Suddenly a huge marble stone appeared in the churchyard, and, on the stone there was a steel anvil. Thrust through the anvil, deep into the stone, was a sword with these words written in gold below the hilt.

WHOSO PULLETH OUT THIS SWORD OF THIS STONE AND ANVIL IS RIGHTWISE KING BORN OF ENGLAND.

Though the lords and nobles tried with all their strength, none could stir the sword. So England was still without a king. The realm fell into great disorder and the strong preyed upon the weak.

In time the miracle of the sword was for-gotten. Weeds sprang up around the anvil, and vines covered the sword, just as they grew wild in the forest.

And now Wart was deep inside the gloomy forest, fighting his way step by step through the tangled underbrush. He ventured on bravely, tripping over countless roots and having his face lashed by countless brambles. At last he came to a tiny clearing in the very heart of the forest.

In the clearing stood a snug little cottage with a thatched roof. A tree that grew close to the cottage stretched its branches so low down that some of them almost touched the roof. And there was the lost arrow, caught in among those branches. Wart stared open-mouthed, amazed at his good fortune.

He neither saw nor heard the fierce wolf ready to spring at him.

The wolf rushed out, growling fiercely. He sprang, but his jaws clashed shut on empty air. For Wart, eager to recover the arrow, had scrambled up the tree just in time.

As Wart climbed up, leaves closed around him on all sides. The wolf was hidden from his view as it prowled around the base of the tree, hoping he might fall.

Peering about, Wart saw the arrow at the far end of a spreading branch. Without another thought he went out towards it.

The branch had begun to bend and creak when at last he had his hand on the arrow. Then it happened. With a great cracking sound a tree branch broke under his weight for the second time that day.

Down fell Wart, head over heels, through the thatched roof.

Wart landed with a thump in front of a table neatly set for tea. "So you did drop in," said a calm voice. "But you are a bit late, you know."

"I—I am?" stammered Wart. He stared across the table at an old gentleman in a strange, pointed hat and a flowing gown.

"My name is Merlin," said the old gentleman. "Come lad, what is your name?"

"My name is Arthur, but everyone calls me Wart."

"Ah!" said Merlin. "Will you have your tea now, Wart?"

Before Wart could answer there was a rustle of soft wings, and an owl rose from his perch near the table and flew across the room.

"Oh!" cried Wart in surprise. "I thought that owl was stuffed."

"Who's stuffed?" said the owl, deeply insulted. "Who? Who?"

"It talks!" cried Wart.

"His name is Archimedes," said Merlin. "He is a highly educated owl."

"I am sorry I mistook you for a stuffed owl," Wart told Archimedes, and from that time on the owl was his friend.

"Sir," Wart said to Merlin, as they drank their tea, "would you mind if I asked you a question? How did you know I would be—?"

"That you would be dropping in?" interrupted Merlin. "Well you see, my boy, I happen to be a wizard."

Wart was very surprised. He had never met a wizard.

"I can see into the future," said Merlin. "Centuries into the future. I have even been there."

"Do you mean that you know everything before it happens?" asked Wart.

"Not everything," said Merlin. "But this I do know—fate has directed you to me so that I may guide you to your rightful place in the world. I am going to be your tutor."

"But I have to get back to the castle!" cried Wart.

"Very well," said Merlin. He stood up and, waving his wand at the four corners of the cottage, he commanded, "Pack up!"

At this all of Merlin's belongings—tables, chairs, chests, china, cutlery, cauldrons, glass retorts, bottles, brooms, benches, and books by the thousands—rose up into the air. There was a great roaring and a hissing noise as the things swirled round and round and got smaller and smaller. When they were small enough they flew into a small leather suitcase standing by the door. The suitcase snapped shut and locked itself securely. And then there was utter silence.

"Come, boy," said Merlin. "I'm going with you to your castle, and it's high time we got started."

Sir Ector let out a loud bellow when he saw Wart enter the great hall of the castle. Although he was very fond of the boy, worry had set the nobleman raging.

"What's the idea of barging off in that infernal forest alone!" he roared. "For that you'll get four hours extra kitchen duty! Report to the cook—hop it, boy! Hop, hop, hop it!"

As Wart scurried off to the kitchen, Merlin greeted Sir Ector and told him why he had come to the castle with his owl and his suitcase.

"Gadzooks!" roared the nobleman. "I'm the one to decide whether or not Wart is getting a proper education!" Then, with a snort, he asked, "Who are you?"

"My name is Merlin," said Merlin, drawing himself up proudly. "And I happen to be the world's most powerful wizard."

Thinking he was dealing with an addled old man, Sir Ector began to laugh at Merlin.

"Hoo-hoo!" he laughed heartily. "The world's most powerful wizard—what a joke!"

"Snow," said Merlin.

Immediately enormous white flakes began to float about in the great hall.

Sir Ector blinked his eyes, then he said, "I know that trick. It's done with mirrors."

"Snow harder," said Merlin.

At once a wintry blast blew through the hall, and the flakes grew bigger and bigger. In an instant Sir Ector's nose was blue with cold and he stood up to his knees in a snow drift.

"That—that's enough," he cried hastily through chattering teeth. "You're welcome to stay, if you like."

The snow stopped immediately.

"You can stay in the northwest tower," cried Sir Ector. "That's the guest room. Just —just make yourself at home."

Merlin smiled and said, "You're very generous."

With the owl flying ahead of him, and the suitcase floating along behind, the old wizard started the long, slow climb up the tower staircase.

Down in the great hall Sir Ector snorted with glee. "Just wait till Merlin sees that guest room—he won't stay here more than two days!"

The guest room in the northwest tower was drafty when the wind blew, and it leaked like a waterspout when it rained. When the owl saw it he wanted to leave at once.

But Merlin said, "This may be a room for unwelcome guests, but we will stay. For Wart has a future, and he must have an education."

"Future!" cried the owl in a bitter voice. "What kind of future can that scrawny little orphan boy have? Tell me that."

"Don't be rude, Archimedes," said Merlin, suddenly stern, "or I'll turn you into a human."

"Oh you wouldn't!" cried Archimedes.

And that was that. They stayed.

One day they saw a knight come galloping into the courtyard far below their tower. From the outcry it was plain to see that he was the bearer of important news. So Merlin sent the owl down to find out what it was.

Sir Ector welcomed the knight and led him into the great hall. With a flip of his wings the owl flew in after them.

The knight cleared his throat and said, "On New Year's Day in London Town there will be a tournament."

"Oh?" said Sir Ector, yawning.

"The winner of the tournament," the knight continued, "will be crowned king of all England."

"What!" cried Sir Ector, leaping up excitedly. And turning to his boys he said, "Kay, lad, did you hear that? You could win it, if you knuckle down to your training. We'll have you knighted by Christmas and off to London.

"And Wart—you will go as Kay's squire."

After flying back with the news, the owl sat quietly and wondered. *Why hold a tournament to choose the king? Isn't there some sort of sword . . . ?*

Merlin said, "If you're thinking of the Sword in the Stone—that is long forgotten."

Days passed, with Sir Ector always watching closely over Kay's training program. There were extra lessons from dawn to dusk, and Kay grumbled without a stop, for now he had no time for his favorite sport, which was to stretch out lazily in the sun.

One day he put on a heavy suit of armor and mounted a horse in order to take a jousting lesson. Grumbling through his visor, Kay held the lance directly forward and charged the practice machine. Wart, who was cranking the machine, flinched as the thumping of the horse's iron hoofs came closer and closer.

The machine spun around with great rapidity, and its spear swept Kay out of his saddle.

"Help!" he cried, flying through the air.

Clang! went his armor as Kay hit a stone wall.

For the rest of that day he lay stretched out in the sun.

"Wart," said Merlin one blazing hot day, "I think it is about time I began *your* lessons." And leading the boy out to the castle moat, he said, "Can you imagine what it is like to be a fish?"

"That's easy," said Wart. "I've done it lots of times."

Merlin waved his wand and said a magic word.

Immediately Wart tumbled off the bank and landed with a splash in the moat.

He had turned into a perch, which is a very small fish. A moment later Merlin, too, had changed into a fish—a graying, elderly trout.

"You are a fish," said Merlin. "But you are not used to being a fish. So you will have to use your head, little perch."

Trying to obey, Wart learned how to swim like a perch.

Suddenly a monstrous pike loomed up and hungrily opened its mouth.

"Merlin!" cried Wart. "Help me! Use magic!"

But Merlin was so startled that he could not think of the magic words that could save Wart. "You must help yourself," he cried. Off darted Wart—and the chase was on!

The pike came closer and closer, its giant body almost invisible in the shadowy murk. With a cunning flick of his tail, Wart vanished altogether behind a clump of weed.

The pike slowly nosed its way into the grassy tangle. Thinking quickly, Wart shot up and did a series of jack-knives that took him high above the water.

The pike was leaping savagely after him when something unexpected happened. There was a sudden rushing noise and, in mid-air, a little claw snatched Wart out of harm's way. It was Archimedes. The owl had come swooping down in the nick of time.

Immediately Wart was a boy again and standing on dry land.

"Well done," said Merlin. "You outwitted that big brute this time!"

As a tiny perch Wart had learned to use his brains. He knew that size and strength weren't the most important things. Now the days passed swiftly, and his education went on.

"I think it is time," said Merlin to him one afternoon, "that you had another lesson."

"Oh, no, sir," said Wart, who was working by himself in the castle kitchen. "I'd better not. I have all this work to do."

Merlin smiled. With a wave of his hand he said, "Clean up."

At once all the dishes that were heaped around, ready to be washed, floated into the air, formed an orderly line and danced over to an enormous bucket of soapy water. A brush and a dishcloth came to life and briskly scrubbed the dishes. Brooms whisked over flagstones while mops sloshed round and round.

"Well," said Merlin, urging Wart towards the door, "a little magic certainly goes a long way, doesn't it? Come, boy, it's time to start your lesson."

But while they were gone, the cook, who had been napping, returned to the kitchen.

THE SWORD IN THE STONE   23

the kitchen brooms still swept flagstones and mops sloshed round and round.

At that moment Wart walked in.

Shaking his fist at the poor boy, Sir Ector roared furiously, "Blast it, Wart! It's all your fault! You brought Merlin here. Just for this —you won't even be Kay's squire!"

A few days later Wart was still downcast. "I can't even hope to be a squire," he told Merlin mournfully. "What's the use of another lesson?"

Merlin chucked him under the chin and said, "You mustn't give up. Come, lad, smile, now."

Wart saw a bird flash by the tower window. With a sigh he said, "I'm tired of being Wart. I wish I were a bird."

In an instant he was a little sparrow.

Archimedes taught Wart to use his wings. They were flying along far from the castle when they were sighted by a hungry hawk.

At once the bird of prey plummeted down at them, its talons pointing directly at the little sparrow.

"Hawk!" cried the owl, terribly alarmed. "Wart, look out!"

With a flick of his wings, Wart darted away. But the hawk followed him, its huge black wings beating strongly.

It was a long and terrible chase, far beyond the strength of a feeble sparrow. Wart, however, escaped the hawk's cruel talons by dropping down a chimney. With the lightest of thumps he fell to the bottom of a cold and cobwebby fireplace.

A gnarled hand lifted him.

A cackling voice said, "Well, look who came to visit me—a scrawny little sparrow with a beakful of soot."

It was Madam Mim, a dreadful old witch.

"Oh, please, I'm not really a sparrow," chirped Wart. "I'm a boy. The great Merlin changed me with his wonderful magic."

At this the witch hissed with anger. "Wonderful magic, bah!" she jeered. "He's

And then Merlin's magic went even further than he had expected.

At the sight of dishes washing themselves, brooms sweeping flagstones with no human hands to guide them, and mops sloshing round and round the self-same way—the cook began to shriek.

Hearing her shrieks, Sir Ector and Kay came rushing in, bravely brandishing swords.

Shouting "To the rescue!" and "Take that!" Sir Ector charged at the lively line of dishes. But after a few steps, he skidded on the wet floor. His arms flailing wildly, the nobleman went sliding over to the enormous bucket. With a great splash he fell in.

The dishcloth and the brush scrubbed Sir Ector with great vigor. Meanwhile all over just a bungler! Obviously you've never heard of me—the marvelous Madam Mim!"

Watching fearfully from the window, Archimedes thought, *If I don't bring Merlin here in time, Mim will surely do something terrible to that boy.*

When Merlin appeared, Madam Mim refused to hand Wart over. Instead, she challenged Merlin to a Wizards' Duel.

She started the duel by turning into a crocodile. Immediately Merlin turned into a tiny turtle and hid inside his hat; and when the crocodile found him there, he turned into a rabbit and nimbly hopped away. Turning into a fox, the witch ran after him.

But then the rabbit turned into a hunting dog. Madam Mim turned from fox to tiger, only to find that the dog had turned into a sharp-clawed crab. Furious at having her nose pinched, she turned into a sharp-horned rhino. As a mouse, Merlin easily eluded the lumbering rhino. But then, calling on her blackest magic, Madam Mim turned into a fearsome, flame-spewing dragon.

Wart gulped with dismay. What could poor Merlin turn into now?

He turned into a rare disease called Purple Pox which was very catching. In an instant the dragon broke out all over in a rash of great purple spots. Anyone sick with Purple

Pox had to stay in bed for two whole weeks. And so Merlin clearly was the winner of the duel.

Time passed.

Winter came and Kay was knighted. He was all ready for the tournament to be held on New Year's Day when suddenly his squire fell ill. So Sir Ector let Wart be Kay's squire after all. And they all set forth proudly to London Town.

The tournament field at London Town was full to the brim on New Year's Day. A great crowd sat in the grandstand. As they watched the tilting, they wondered which brave knight would win and so become their king.

Sir Ector clapped Kay on the shoulder. "You'll win, boy!" he cried. "Dash it all, I feel it in my bones!"

Just then there came a dismal moan from Wart. In his excitement he had forgotten Kay's sword. It was back at the inn where they had slept.

Kay was furious when he heard this. "You bungling little fool!" he cried.

"Oh, please, Kay," said Wart. "I'll fetch it for you."

"You'd better fetch it!" Kay shouted after him as he ran off. "Or don't you dare come back!"

Wart ran his fastest, but when he got to the inn it was closed. Everyone had gone to the tournament.

A sword! He had to have a sword!

Wart ran frantically along the street until he came to a quiet churchyard. And there was a heavy stone with an anvil on it, and a gleaming sword was stuck through the anvil.

With a sigh of relief Wart ran up to the sword, drew it out gently, and carried it back to the tournament field.

"But *that's* not Kay's sword," said Sir Ector when he saw it.

Noticing some letters written in gold below the hilt, Sir Ector took the sword from Wart's hands. He held it closely and read:

WHOSO PULLETH OUT THIS SWORD OF THIS STONE AND ANVIL IS RIGHTWISE KING BORN OF ENGLAND.

The nobleman turned white, for suddenly he remembered the old story of the Sword in the Stone.

"Wart," he said hoarsely, "where did you get this?"

"Outside a church," said Wart. "It was stuck in an anvil."

By now a crowd of noblemen had gathered around. They all looked at the sword and they looked at Wart.

"Wart," said Sir Ector, his voice still hoarse, "we will all go back to the church at once."

At the church Wart replaced the sword in the stone, then gently drew it out again. But when Kay pulled at it with all his strength, he could not stir the sword. A sigh of wonder rose from the crowd.

Sir Ector, who was a very loyal Englishman, kneeled down before Wart. He forced Kay to kneel down, too.

"Please don't," said Wart. "Let me help you up, sir."

Someone asked, "What's the lad's name?"

"Wart," said Kay.

"Nonsense," snapped Archimedes. "His real name is Arthur."

At this there was a clap of thunder and Merlin made one of his magical appearances. "King Arthur!" he said. "So that's who dropped in to tea!"

"Hail King Arthur!" roared the crowd. "Long live King Arthur!"

As it happens, King Arthur lived very long. What is more important—he was a great and very noble king.

ALICE IN WONDERLAND MEETS THE WHITE RABBIT

Do you know where Wonderland is? It is the place you visit in your dreams, the strange and wondrous place where nothing is as it seems. It was in Wonderland that Alice met the White Rabbit.

He was hurrying across the meadow, looking at his pocket watch and saying to himself: "I'm late, I'm late, for a very important date.

"I'm in a rabbit stew, oh oh! Can't even say good-bye—hello! I'm late, I'm late, I'm late!"

He hopped across the brook and disappeared into a hollow tree.

"That's curious," said Alice. "A rabbit who wears a waistcoat, and carries a watch, and can talk!

"He's in such a hurry, he must be going to a party. I surely would like to go, too."

So Alice followed him.

"What a peculiar place to give a party," she thought as she pushed her way into the hollow tree.

But before she could think any more, she began to slide on some slippery white pebbles inside. And then she began to fall!

"Curious and curiouser!" said Alice as she floated slowly down, past cupboards and lamps, a rocking chair, past clocks and mirrors she met in mid-air.

By the time she reached the bottom the White Rabbit was disappearing through a little door. The door was much too small for Alice to follow him.

So on she wandered through Wonderland, all by her lonely self.

At last she reached a neat little house in the woods, with pink shutters and a little front door that opened and—out came the White Rabbit!

"Oh, my twitching whiskers!" he was saying to himself. He seemed very much upset. Then he looked up and saw Alice standing there.

"Mary Ann!" he said sharply. "Why, Mary Ann, what are you doing here? Well, don't just do something, stand there! No, go get my gloves. I'm very late!"

"But late for what?" Alice began to ask.

"My gloves!" said the White Rabbit firmly. And Alice dutifully went to look for them, though she knew she wasn't Mary Ann!

When she came back, the White Rabbit was just disappearing through the woods again.

So off went Alice, trying to follow him through that strange, mixed-up Wonderland.

She met Tweedledee and Tweedledum, a funny little pair.

She joined a mad tea party with the Mad Hatter and the March Hare.

Poor Alice! She was all alone in Wonderland, where nothing was just what it seemed. (You know how things are in dreams!)

Whenever she ate a bite of cake or took a sip to drink, she would shoot up tall or grow so tiny she was sometimes afraid she would vanish quite away.

She met other animals, yes, indeed, strange talking animals, too. They tried to be as helpful as they could. But they couldn't help her find the White Rabbit.

"And I really must find him," Alice thought, though she wasn't sure just why.

She met a Cheshire cat who faded in and out of sight. And one strange creature—Jabberwock—whose eyes flamed in the night.

They all were very kind, but they could not show Alice the way, until:

"There *is* a short cut," she heard the Cheshire cat say. So Alice took it.

The short cut led into a garden where gardeners were busy painting roses red.

"We must hurry," they said, "for the Queen is coming!"

And sure enough, a trumpet blew, and a voice called:

"Make way for the Queen of Hearts!"

Then out came a grand procession. And who should be the royal trumpeter for the cross-looking Queen but the White Rabbit.

"Well!" said Alice. "So this is why he was hurrying so!"

"Who are you?" snapped the Queen. "Do you play croquet?"

"I'm Alice. And I'm just on my way home. Thank you for the invitation, but I really mustn't stay."

"So!" cried the Queen. "So she won't play! Off with her head then!"

But Alice was tired of Wonderland now, and all its nonsensical ways.

"Pooh!" she said. "I'm not frightened of you. You're nothing but a pack of cards."

And with that she ran back through that land of dreams, back to the river bank where she had fallen asleep.

"Hm," she said, as she rubbed her eyes. "I'm glad to be back where things are what they seem. I've had quite enough for now of Wonderland!"

101 DALMATIANS

A DAMP BEGINNING

NOT LONG ago there lived in London a Dalmatian called Pongo. Pongo had a human "pet," Roger Radcliff. Like most humans, Roger thought that people owned their dogs. But like most dogs, Pongo knew better.

The two young bachelors would probably have lived on in their cluttered little flat, if Pongo hadn't happened to look out of the window one fine spring day.

He was looking out of the window because he was tired of looking at the mess inside the flat. Dirty coffee cups were piled high on the mantelpiece. One of Roger's ties was draped over the lampshade. And papers were scattered all over the floor. Roger was a song writer, and as he sat at the piano, humming and playing tunes, he was apt to forget about such unimportant things as waste-paper baskets and ashtrays.

"Something has to be done," thought Pongo, as he gazed out of the window.

Suddenly Pongo sat up very straight. A beautiful Dalmatian, her head carried high, was trotting demurely past the window. With her was an equally beautiful lady.

"That's it!" thought Pongo. "We need mates. Preferably tidy ones, and those two look just right."

It was just four-fifteen by the battered old clock on the mantel. Pongo always took Roger for a walk promptly at five o'clock. It was an easy matter for Pongo to turn the hands of the clock forward with his nose. Then he barked to attract Roger's attention.

"Hmm," said Roger, "is it five already?" He absent-mindedly set his watch hands to match those of the clock, and then he searched for his hat.

"Time for your walk in the park, old boy," said Roger. "Now where is your leash?" But Pongo was already holding it in his mouth, his tail wagging joyfully.

"We must hurry," thought Pongo, "or we'll be too far behind." And as Roger opened the door, the dog leaped forward with a bound, tugging his pet behind him.

Pongo headed for the park, pulling so hard on the leash that Roger almost had to run to keep up with him.

"Pongo, boy," cried Roger. "Take it easy. What's the hurry?"

But the dog hurried on, looking this way and that, darting down side paths and peering into shaded nooks. And suddenly he found them. The girl was seated on a bench reading, and the beautiful Dalmatian was by her side, watching the swans on the lake. It was a perfect situation, Pongo knew, if he could only take advantage of it.

"I can't depend on Roger," thought Pongo. "I know what he'll do. He'll settle down on the grass and puff his pipe, and that will be it. It's up to me."

Pongo led Roger slowly past the bench. Roger was staring straight ahead, but the girl looked up from her book and her dog cast Pongo a shy glance. Then Roger did exactly what Pongo had expected. He sat down on the grass, with his back to the girl, and slowly puffed his pipe.

Quickly Pongo snatched Roger's hat from his head and started to cavort about the bench.

"Pongo, you crazy hound!" shouted Roger. "Come on. Let's have it back, boy."

But Pongo continued his gamboling, and finally dropped his hat on the young lady's bench.

It worked. Roger had finally seen the girl. But as Pongo continued to bark wildly, chase pigeons, and generally show off, the girl gave a sigh of exasperation and closed her book.

"Come, Perdita," she called to her dog. "There's no use trying to read." They rose to leave.

Roger caught Pongo with a flying tackle, and snapped the leash onto his collar.

"Come on, you old renegade," he said. "We're going home. You know, Pongo, you're getting to be quite a rascal. What's come over you?" Roger turned resolutely toward home.

But Pongo wasn't giving up without one more try. In desperation he ran around the girl, then wheeled back in a circle towards Roger, winding the two of them up in his leash.

"Oh! I beg your pardon! So sorry . . . I . . ." stammered Roger, as he and the girl struggled to keep their balance.

"Well, I never in all my life . . ." the girl started to say, but the rest of her words were lost in a loud SPLASH! Roger and the girl had fallen into the lake. The girl's dog looked on in shocked silence, while Pongo, trying to make amends, retrieved the girl's hat. It was a catastrophe.

"Oh," wailed the girl. "My . . . my new spring suit. And . . . and my new hat!"

Roger was flustered and contrite. "Please," he said, "let me help you up. I'm so sorry. My dog has never acted this way before."

"Never mind! Never mind!" said the girl. "Just go away."

She reached into her purse for a handkerchief to dry her face, but the handkerchief was at wet as the rest of her.

"Here," said Roger gallantly, as he reached into his pocket. "Take mine."

Roger made a ridiculous picture as he stood damply in the pond, holding out a dripping kerchief. The girl began to giggle . . . then to laugh. Roger grinned sheepishly. Finally, both of them burst into shrieks of laughter.

Pongo could hardly believe his ears. Somehow his plan had worked.

"There's no figuring out humans," he thought, "or females of any kind for that matter." For the girl's dog was looking at him shyly . . . and he knew he'd been forgiven.

CRUELLA DE VIL

After that, the two dogs and their pets often walked together in the park, and the meeting that had begun in so cold and wet a fashion deepened into warm affection.

The girl's name, Pongo learned, was Anita. Her dog was Perdita, and Pongo thought it the prettiest name he had ever heard.

It wasn't long before Roger and Anita were married, an arrangement that suited Pongo and Perdita admirably.

The four of them moved into a small house near the park. It was a modest little house, but just right for two couples who were starting out. Roger worked at his music on the top floor, in quarters considerably tidier than the old bachelor flat. There was now a round little dumpling of a maid called Nanny, who was a wonderful cook and housekeeper. She was such a kind and understanding soul that Pongo often said he considered her almost canine.

Life in the little flat was pleasant and uneventful for the first few months. And then Cruella De Vil began to pay them visits.

She was a strange woman, an old school friend of Anita's. Roger heartily disliked her, and as for Pongo and Perdita—their instinct was to stay as far away from her as possible.

One day Roger was searching for suitable words to fit his new melody. A screech of brakes drew him to the window, and he groaned, "There she is again—Cruella De Vil."

He turned back to his piano, then suddenly he let out a wild yell.

"Cruella! Cruella De Vil! That's it!"

He started to sing.

"Cruella De Vil . . . Cruella De Vil . . .
If she doesn't scare you, no evil thing will.
She's like a spider waiting for the kill . . .
Cruella . . . Cruella De Vil . . ."

"Shh, Roger. She'll hear you," said Anita, as Cruella swept into the house, trailing her furs behind her.

"Darling, how are you?" gushed Cruella. "And how are your little spotted friends?" She looked thoughtfully at Perdita and Pongo. "They have such *perfectly* beautiful coats." The two dogs backed away nervously. "When do you expect the puppies, and how many of them?"

"Oh, six or seven," answered Anita. "And sometimes as many as nine or ten. But we won't know for another three weeks or so."

Cruella smiled a crafty smile. "Let me know when they arrive, won't you dear?"

she said, and she departed with a swish of her black and white furs.

"Oh Pongo," said Perdita, "what does it mean? Why does she want our puppies? That's all she's after, I know it."

"Don't worry, Perdy," soothed Pongo. "Nothing's going to happen to them. Our pets will see to that."

But Perdita still felt terrified of Cruella.

PUPPIES—AND MORE PUPPIES

The puppies were born one wild and stormy night late in October. Pongo and Roger waited anxiously in the kitchen, while Nanny excitedly announced the arrival of first eight puppies . . . then two more . . . then three additional ones, and finally, fifteen in all.

"Fifteen!" exclaimed Roger. "Pongo, old boy! Can you imagine? FIFTEEN!"

There was a flash of lightning and a roll of thunder, and Cruella De Vil burst unannounced into the room.

"Fifteen puppies!" she cried. "How marvelous! How perfectly, perfectly marvelous!" Before anyone could stop her, she strode over to Perdita's basket and looked down at the puppies.

"Why, they're mongrels! No spots! No spots at all!" cried Cruella in disgust.

"They are *not* mongrels," snapped Nanny Cook. "They'll get their spots. Just wait and see."

"That's right," added Anita. "They'll have their spots in a few weeks."

Cruella smiled an evil smile and reached into her purse for a checkbook.

"Oh, well," she said. "In that case I'll take them all—the whole litter. Just name your price."

"I'm afraid we can't give them up," answered Anita. "Perdita and Pongo would be heartbroken."

"Don't be ridiculous," snapped Cruella. "You can't possibly afford to keep them. You can hardly feed yourselves. What are you going to live on—Roger's songs?" She laughed rudely. "Come now, Anita, when can the puppies leave their mother? In two weeks? Three weeks?"

Roger had been fuming in the background. But now, though he trembled a bit, he stepped forward and stammered:

"We're *not* selling the pup—puppies. N—not a sing—single one—understand? And that's f—final!"

"Why, you horrible man!" screeched Cruella. "*Keep* the little beasts for all I care. But I warn you—I'll get even with you. You *fools*—you *idiots!*" And, stalking out of the house, Cruella slammed the door behind her, so hard that its pane of glass shattered in a hundred pieces.

"Roger," cried Anita joyously, "you were magnificent, darling!"

Nanny Cook clasped her hands in glee. "Oh," she cried, "he was a blooming hero, ma'am! Indeed, he was a blooming hero!"

Quickly, Pongo ran to break the good news to Perdita.

"Perdy," he cried. "We're keeping the puppies—every single one of them. My old pet, Roger, told off that Cruella woman. She's gone! Gone for good!"

"Oh, Pongo," sighed Perdita. "I don't think I've ever been so happy."

THE DOGNAPPERS

They would not have been so happy had they known what Cruella was planning. Over a grimy table in the back room of a tavern, Cruella was talking to two villainous-looking men. One was tall and thin, the other short and fat, but both had shifty eyes and an evil look about them. These were the Baduns, Jasper and Horace.

"Listen carefully to me, you two," said Cruella sternly. "I must have those Dalmatian puppies. Now let me explain my plan to you. . . ."

All was happy, if not exactly quiet, in the little house until one snowy night in December. The puppies had grown, and were now tumbling all over the house. They were more than a handful for Pongo and Perdita. But they loved their pups dearly—all fifteen of them.

That evening, the pups had been particularly rowdy. It was with a sigh of relief that Perdita at last found the smallest pup, Lucky, and tucked him safely into the basket with the others. They were soon all asleep.

"Come on, Perdy," said Pongo. "It's time for our walk."

They brought their leashes to Roger and Anita, and the four of them set out into the park.

In a rickety little truck around the corner, the two Baduns watched.

"There they go for their evening walk," said Jasper.

"Yes," answered Horace, "and nobody home but the little old cook. Let's get on with our business." Stepping up to the front door, Horace pressed the doorbell, and Nanny came to answer the ring.

"We're here to inspect the wiring and the switches," said the Baduns. "We're from the electric company."

"We didn't call for any inspection," said Nanny, and started to close the door.

"It's for your own safety, ma'am," said Horace, and the two ruffians shouldered their way into the house.

"What's the matter with you two?" shouted the furious Nanny. "If you don't get out of this house, I'll call the police."

But while Nanny attached herself firmly to one of the Baduns' coattails and chased him up and down the stairs, the other had accomplished his purpose. In just a matter of moments, the two villains had left through the front door as quickly as they had entered.

"Why, those good-for-nothing hoodlums," sputtered Nanny. "They're nothing but common sneak thieves. I'll bet they've made off with the best silver." She rushed to look. But the silver was undisturbed.

"They were up to something, I'll be bound," she said. "They just wouldn't be— OH . . . THE PUPPIES . . . THE PUPPIES! THEY'RE GONE!"

Panic-stricken, Nanny rushed into the street, but it was too late. The Baduns and their truck and the fifteen puppies had disappeared around the corner.

"Those scoundrels! They took the puppies," cried Nanny. "POLICE! HELP! Oh, can't anybody hear me?"

No one did, and Nanny sank, sobbing, to the curb.

THE TWILIGHT BARK

The papers were full of the news the next morning. "DOGNAPPING. FIFTEEN PUPPIES STOLEN!" said the headlines. There were pictures of the puppies and their parents, and photos of Anita and Roger. Cruella grinned as she saw the pictures.

"Anita and her bashful Beethoven—pipe and all!" She laughed. "Oh, Roger. What a fool you are!"

The ring of the phone interrupted her gleeful perusal of the papers. It was one of the Baduns, and he was frightened.

"We want our money," said Jasper. "The story is in all the papers—with pictures and all. We're getting out of this!"

"Idiot!" shrieked Cruella. "How dare you call me here! You'll get not one penny until the job's finished. Do you hear?" She slammed down the phone.

But she picked it up again almost immediately.

"Oh, Anita. What a dreadful thing!" she cooed. "I just saw the papers. I couldn't believe it—about the stolen puppies."

"Yes, Cruella," answered Anita. "It was a shock. We're doing everything possible. We even called Scotland Yard, but nothing's been found out yet."

"She's still Number One Suspect in my book," grumbled Roger when Anita had put the phone down. "She's been investigated by Scotland Yard and is supposedly innocent . . . but I don't know . . ."

Pongo looked at them sadly and walked back to Perdita.

"Perdy," he said, "I'm afraid our pets are getting nowhere in their search for our puppies. It looks as if it's up to us."

Perdita was tearful.

"Oh, Pongo!" she wept. "Isn't there any hope?"

"Yes," replied Pongo. *The Twilight Bark.*"

"But it's just a gossip chain," began Perdita.

"It's still the fastest way to send news," said Pongo. "And if our puppies are anywhere in the city, the London dogs will know. We'll send the word *tonight*."

It was late and almost dark when Roger and Anita led the two Dalmatians into the park and to the top of Primrose Hill.

Pongo barked the alert—three loud barks and a long howl. At first there was no reply, but finally there came an answer.

"Perdy," said Pongo. "We're in luck. It's the Great Dane over at Hampstead." And Pongo barked out the message.

"Pongo! Quiet, boy!" exclaimed Roger. "Do you want to stir up the whole neighborhood? Come on, old fellow. We're going home."

But the message had been delivered.

Over at Hampstead, the Great Dane was trying to decode the message. A little terrier frisked impatiently about him, bursting with questions: "What is it, Danny? Who's on the telegraph?"

"It's Pongo, Regents Park. It's an all-dog alert," answered Danny.

"What's it all about? What's the word, Danny?" urged the small dog.

"Wait a minute," said Danny, as he translated the barks and yips and howls into the final understandable message. "Well, now! That *is* something. Fifteen puppies stolen— Dalmatians!"

"*Fifteen* puppies?" said the terrier. "Stolen?"

"Yes," replied the Great Dane. "No one knows who did it. Not a clue. Not a trace. They've even called Scotland Yard. The humans have tried everything. Now it's up to us dogs to find them, through the Twilight Bark. I'll send the alert."

The big dog's voice boomed into the night: three loud barks and a long howl. Soon the answering barks started coming in from miles away, every dog wanting to hear the latest news.

Big Danny barked out the message, and from setter to collie, from bulldog to Labrador, the news was relayed.

In a London back alley two old mongrels heard the message as they rummaged through the rubbish cans for food. Said one: "Those puppies aren't in London! They could be anywhere from Plymouth to Newcastle by now."

"Brucey, old lad," said the other, "what do you say we send the word all over England?"

"That's an idea," agreed the first. "I'll leg it for the station at Charing Cross. There are always some dogs going out by freight."

"I'll take the waterfront and tell all the barge dogs," said the other. "Shake a leg, mate." At the River Thames, a small dog on a passing barge barked him a greeting, and in return received Pongo's message as the barge slowly moved by.

The little barge dog wasted no time. As his vessel moved slowly along the moonlit river, he barked the alert at intervals, and to answering greetings he sent out Pongo's message.

The message finally reached the ears of an old hound standing on a hill. "What's going on, Towser?" asked an inquisitive goose, as she joined him on the hilltop. "What's all the gossip?"

" 'Tain't gossip, Lucy," he answered. "It's a message all the way from London. Fifteen puppies have been stolen."

"There are no puppies around here," answered the goose. "Except those of Ellen's. And they're all grown up now."

"Then it's up to me to send the word along," answered the old hound. "It'll be up to me to reach the Colonel. He's the only one within barking range."

The goose looked up at the dark night sky. "You'll never reach him at this hour," she warned, waddling off down the hill.

"I can try," said Towser to himself. "I'll bark all night if I have to." He cleared his throat, and once again the alert call went through the night.

HELL HALL

In a stable a few miles away, a retired army horse named Captain was contentedly munching hay. "Hmm," he whinnied, as he heard distant barking. "Sounds like Towser. It's an alert!" He turned to the cat who lay sleeping peacefully on his broad back.

"Sergeant! Sergeant Tibs! Wake up!" he neighed. "A barking signal—an alert. Report to the Colonel at once."

"Yes, sir," said the cat. "Right away, sir." Tibs scampered into the dim shadows of the hayloft in search of his commanding officer.

The Colonel, a gruff old sheepdog, emerged with sleepy eyes and tousled gray hair from a pile of hay.

"Now look here, Tibs," he grumbled, "what's the idea of barging in at this hour of the night?"

"It's an alert, sir," answered Sergeant Tibs. "It's from old Towser down at Withermarsh, sir." The Colonel cocked a long, fuzzy ear toward the barking.

"By Jove," he grunted. "Yes. So it is. I'll see what he wants." His foghorn voice sounded over the hills, and before long there was an answering bark.

"Let's see," said the Colonel. "One long howl . . . two short . . . one yip and a woof. Hmmm . . . I'll have to decode that."

The Colonel listened again. "The next sounds like a number. Four . . . no . . . five woofs. Three fives are thirteen. . . ."

Sergeant Tibs interrupted politely: "That's fifteen, sir." The distant barking continued.

The Colonel was having trouble with his decoding. He lifted his right ear still higher and strained toward the direction of the far-off sounds.

"Hmmm," he murmured. "Dot . . . spot . . . spotted . . . puddings . . . er . . . poodles. Puddles . . . fifteen spotted puddles stolen! Oh, balderdash!" The Colonel glared at the Captain and Sergeant Tibs.

"Try it again, sir," urged Sergeant Tibs. "Ask them to repeat the message."

"Could it be *puppies*, sir?" said Sergeant Tibs, when the distant barking continued. "Fifteen stolen puppies? And that reminds me—two nights ago I heard puppy-barking over at Hell Hall, the old deserted De Vil mansion."

"Nonsense, Tibs!" growled the Colonel. "Nobody's lived there for years!"

The Captain switched his long tail. "Hold on," he said. "Look! There's smoke coming from the chimney."

The Colonel turned to look. "By Jove, so there is! So there is! Humph! I suppose we'll have to investigate!"

With the cat riding on his back, the Colonel plowed through the snow toward the old ruin that once had been a proud mansion.

Tibs, who had heard many tales of the old house being haunted, had to gather up all his courage to climb the tree that stood near the wall. From the wall he leaped onto a narrow ledge, and crept along it till he reached a broken window pane. Carefully, he let himself in.

The house was dark, but suddenly Tibs saw a shaft of light shining under a door. Cautiously he peered into the room beyond.

In a jumble of musty furniture, half-eaten food and odds and ends of their own belongings, lounged two of the most villainous rascals Tibs had even seen.

They were watching a show on a brand-new television set.

But the amazing thing about the room was that, on the floor, on chairs and benches, and curled up on the faded rugs, were *dozens* and *dozens* of *Dalmatian puppies*.

Tibs patiently counted them. He was searching for *fifteen* puppies . . . and here were ninety-nine of them.

"Psst! Youngster!" he whispered to the nearest one. "Are you one of the fifteen stolen puppies?"

"No," the puppy replied. "Most of us came from pet shops in London. But those little ones in front of the television set all have names and collars. Are they the ones you're looking for?"

Tibs was certain that they were. Quickly he retraced his steps to where the Colonel waited and told him the news.

SERGEANT TIBS TO THE RESCUE

The Colonel barked the message to old Towser, who in turn passed it on to a barge dog. From dog to dog the news went on its way toward distant London. Pongo was listening anxiously at the window when he heard Big Danny's voice.

"What is it, Pongo?" asked Perdita.

"It's the Great Dane," answered Pongo. "He has news for us. He'll meet us at Primrose Hill."

"But how will we get out?" said Perdita. She knew it wasn't nearly time for their evening walk.

"Through the back bedroom window," replied Pongo. "It's always open a wee bit. Come on." Pongo raised the window sash with his nose. In an instant the two Dalmatians had jumped from a low roof to the ground, scaled the fence and were on their way to the park. There the Great Dane waited.

"The Pongos! You've made it," he exclaimed with relief. "Good. Your puppies have been found somewhere north of here—in Suffolk."

"Thank heaven!" said Perdita. "Are they all right? Are they safe?"

"That I can't say," replied the big dog. "But I do have a plan to reach them. Can you leave tonight?"

"Yes, of course," said Pongo. "We can leave right away."

The Dane nodded his massive head with satisfaction, and related his plans as the three trotted down the hill.

"I'll go with you as far as Camden Road and give instructions. It's a long trip. Can you read road signs?"

Pongo said that he could, and was rewarded by an admiring look from Perdita.

"When you reach Withermarsh get in touch with old Towser. He'll direct you to the Colonel, and the Colonel will take you to the De Vil place."

"De Vil!" exclaimed Perdita. "Oh, Pongo. It was her!"

"Someone you know?" asked the Great Dane.

"Sorry, sir," answered Pongo, "no time to explain. Oh, I hope we're not too late." And Perdita and Pongo were on their way, running with all their might.

"Good luck, Pongos," barked the Great Dane after them. "If you lose your way, contact the barking chain. They'll be standing by to hear from you."

All night they traveled, pausing only to check their directions with dogs who were awaiting them at various points along the way. During the day they slept, exhausted.

The Colonel and Sergeant Tibs nervously paced the floor of their stable. "What has happened to them?" said the Colonel. "They should have been here by now."

A long red and black car, driven like the wind, shot down the nearby road and screeched to a stop in front of Hell Hall.

"Blast it all," grumbled the Colonel. "Better see what's up, Tibs. On the double, man! On the double!" Tibs jumped on the Colonel's back, and the two started once again plowing through the snow drifts toward the forbidding mansion.

Tibs chose his old route of entry, and got to the living room door just in time to hear Cruella De Vil say to the Baduns,

"I've got no time to argue! I tell you, it's got to be done tonight!"

"But the pups ain't big enough," Horace said. "You couldn't get a half dozen coats out of the whole kaboodle!"

Sergeant Tibs was aghast.

"Coats—dog-skin coats!" he groaned. "So that's it!"

"Now listen," shouted Cruella, "I'll be back in the morning—and the job had better be done. Do you understand?" With a great slam of the door, she was gone.

Tibs squeezed himself through a hole next to the door and nudged the nearest puppies.

"You'd better get out of here if you want to save your skins," he whispered. "There's a hole in the wall—there by the door. Come on. Shake a leg."

Luckily, Horace and Jasper were absorbed in their favorite television show. Otherwise they would surely have seen the procession of puppies that squeezed, one by one, through the small hole.

Tibs ran from end to end of the line, trying to keep the puppies in order. "Faster! Faster!" he urged. "One at a time!"

Pushing and squeezing and struggling, the

pups got through the hole. The television show was almost at an end. At any moment the Baduns might look around and discover them.

Finally, the last pup in the line scrambled through to safety. But no, there was still one left! Tibs groaned as he saw him, sitting right in front of the television set, watching the show.

How was he to reach him without warning Horace and Jasper?

Tibs' problem was solved when Jasper disgustedly picked up the puppy and tossed him out of the way.

Tibs grabbed the puppy and frantically tried to squeeze him through the hole, just as the television show ended.

The hole was small, and the puppy was large, and he couldn't help giving out a little yip as Tibs struggled to force him through.

"Hey! Horace—look!" shouted Jasper, as he turned around and saw the empty room. "The pups are gone! They flew the coop! Right out through that little hole—there! Grab a flashlight!"

Jasper grabbed a poker from the fireplace, and the two Baduns burst into the hallway.

Behind them, up the stairs, the puppies were just turning the corner. But the last puppy slipped on the top stair, bounced down a step and yipped in surprise.

"There they go,—up the stairs," shouted Jasper.

The puppies were nowhere to be seen.

"Here, puppies," said Jasper coaxingly. "Come here, now. Don't go hiding from your old Uncle Jasper. I won't hurt you."

"But I thought we were going to pop them off," said Horace.

"Shhh!" admonished Jasper. "Shut up! Take a squint in that room and I'll take these other two rooms."

Sergeant Tibs had herded the puppies under an enormous bed, but he knew that they wouldn't be safe for long. Jasper burst into the room, and the bright beam of his flashlight suddenly lit up their hiding place. To Jasper, it seemed that there was a veritable explosion of small dogs, as Tibs and the puppies knocked him off his feet and stampeded over him.

"It's that mangy tabby cat!" cried the infuriated Jasper. "He's the ring leader. Head them off, Horace—head them off!"

Tibs and the puppies raced down the stairs. The Colonel, watching outside a window, blinked as he saw the stream of puppies with the Baduns in close pursuit. "I say, Sergeant, wait a moment!" he called.

"No time to explain!" shouted Tibs as he dashed past. Then he added politely, "Sorry, sir. Busy, sir."

It was just at this moment that Pongo and Perdita, after a long and wearisome journey, hesitated at the crossroads. Perdita was discouraged. "Pongo, Pongo," she wailed. "I'm afraid we're lost."

"I don't think so, Perdy. It can't be far," said Pongo. Once more he barked the alert message. The Colonel heard it.

"By Jove," he exclaimed. "It's the Pongos —at last!"

He raced out to meet them.

"Are—are you the Colonel?" asked Pongo. "Our puppies? Are they all right?"

"No time to explain," answered the old sheepdog. "I'm afraid there's trouble. Big hullaballoo. Come along. Follow me."

The three hurried off towards Hell Hall.

The Colonel was right. There *was* trouble.

Tibs and the puppies were backed up in a corner, and the Baduns were standing menacingly over them.

Jasper was jubilant. "Ha!" he gloated. "Now we got them, Horace. They've finally run out of room. Now we can do the job."

But before either of them could land a blow, there was a crash of splintering glass as Pongo and Perdita leaped through a window into the room.

The Baduns whirled around in surprise.

"Hey, what's this!" cried Jasper. Then he gave a bellow as Pongo made a flying leap for his leg.

"Looks like a couple of spotted hyenas!" croaked Horace.

There was a wild melee of swinging clubs and flying bodies. The dogs were quicker and more agile than the Baduns, and in the confusion the men landed more blows on each other than on the Dalmatians. But Jasper connected with a lucky kick, and Pongo crashed into the door, where he lay dazed.

"There, you mangy mongrel!" shouted Jasper. "I'll knock your blinking block off!" He swung his heavy poker, but a bite from Perdita spoiled his aim, and his blow smashed through the old, crumbling door as Pongo

returned to the fray. The Colonel poked his head through the hole.

"Go on, Tibs!" he thundered. "Give them what for!"

"No, Colonel, no!" panted Tibs, seeing a way of escape. "Retreat! Retreat!"

The Colonel saw immediately that Tibs was right, for the fight in the room was growing wilder by the minute.

"Yes, yes! Retreat!" the old sheepdog agreed.

Quick as a cat, Tibs herded the puppies through the broken door, and the long line of them floundered through the drifts on their way to the Captain's stable.

There was no doubt about it, the Baduns were getting the worst of the fight. Perdita pulled a rug from under Horace, who fell into the smouldering fireplace. He emerged, shrieking, and collided with Jasper. The two landed against the wall, the ancient house shook, and the villains were bombarded with a shower of falling plaster.

"Come on, Perdy. Let's go," said Pongo, and the two dashed after the trail of the puppies as the Baduns struggled to get out of the debris that covered them.

Jasper shook himself, furious. "I'll skin every one of those little spotted fiends, if it's the last thing I do."

The Colonel, Sergeant Tibs and all the Dalmatians had vanished, but their trail led unmistakably over the hill to the Captain's stable. Arming themselves with poker and chair leg, the Baduns ran to their truck.

REUNION

It was a warm reunion in the stable, with all the fifteen puppies talking at once, and Perdita and Pongo were abrim with delight.

"All fifteen here?" anxiously asked Pongo.

"More than twice that many, lad," said Lucky. "Now there are ninety-nine!"

"Uh—ni—*ninety-nine!*" stuttered Pongo. He and Perdita stared aghast at the sea of Dalmatian puppies that filled the stable. "What on earth would Cruella De Vil want with so many?"

"She was going to make *coats* out of us," blurted out one puppy. Pongo and Perdita were shocked into silence. Sergeant Tibs affirmed the puppy's startling news. "That's right!" he said solemnly. "*Dog-skin* coats."

The kindly old Colonel huffed and spluttered. "Oh, come now, Tibs! Dog-skin coats, indeed. I don't believe it!"

Sergeant Tibs stood his ground. "It's true, sir," the cat insisted. "I heard the Baduns and Cruella talking about it at Hell Hall."

Pongo and Perdita stood perplexed, their fifteen puppies gathered about them in a circle. The other puppies in the room waited and listened anxiously.

"Cruella's a devil—a witch!" cried Perdita. "Oh, Pongo, what will we do?"

"We have to get back to London somehow," Pongo said. "And we'll have to take the other puppies, too, Perdy. *All* of them. Our human pets would never turn them out."

The big horse, Captain, turned from his vantage point by the window. "Colonel, sir," he said. "Lights on the road. It's a truck headed this way." The Colonel bristled.

"It's the Baduns . . . Horace and Jasper," he said. "They're following our tracks." He drew himself to his full height. "Well," he thundered, "we've got them out-numbered, Tibs! When I give the signal, we'll attack!"

Sergeant Tibs saluted respectfully. "Oh, Colonel, sir, I'm afraid that would be disastrous, sir."

"He's right, Colonel," said Pongo. "We'd better make a run for it."

"Better be off," urged the Captain, from his post at the window. "Here they come."

"Thank you, Sergeant, Colonel, Captain. Bless you all," said Perdita. "How can we possibly repay you for everything you've done?"

"It was nothing," said the Colonel gruffly. "All in the line of duty, you know."

The headlights of the approaching Baduns' truck drew nearer, and the puppies, led by Perdita, filed out of the back door and across the pasture. Pongo drew up the rear.

"Good luck, Pongos," called Sergeant Tibs and the Captain.

"Yes. Good luck," added the Colonel, as he watched Horace and Jasper advance from their truck. "Don't worry. We'll hold the Baduns to the bitter end."

Growling, the shaggy old dog confronted the two men at the stable door. Dodging the blows hurled at him by Horace and Jasper, he retreated slowly and grudgingly into the stable's dark interior. The Baduns stared, amazed. There was no sign of the Dalmatians. The Colonel had held the men back long enough for the Pongos and the throng of youngsters to make their escape.

Now it was the Captain's turn to further delay the Baduns. The hoofs of the big horse shot out, and Horace sailed through the air and crashed through the stable wall.

"Splendid, Captain!" shouted Tibs. "Now for the other one!" With a second flash of his hoofs, the old horse booted Jasper across the stable to join his companion. But as Jasper picked himself up out of the snow, he saw the wide trail of dog tracks that led over the hill.

"Hey, there they go, the little sneaks!" he yelped. "Come on, Horace. Back to the truck. We'll head them off in half a mile."

Pongo realized their tracks in the snow would be easy to follow, and he was worried. But suddenly luck fell in their way—a frozen creek. Its smooth, icy surface would leave no sign of their passing. Slipping and sliding, he and Perdita herded their floundering group onto the ice. They gained the safety of the underside of a stone bridge just as the pursuing Baduns pulled their truck to a stop on the road overhead. One pup skidded almost into the Baduns' view, but Pongo pulled it back to safety. They could hear Jasper and Horace talking:

"Jasper, I've been thinking. What if those dogs went down the frozen creek so as not to leave their tracks?"

"Aw, Horace, you idiot!" retorted Jasper. "Dogs aren't that smart!" With a grinding of gears, the truck went on. Pongo waited until it had disappeared from view.

"All clear, Perdy," he announced, and they continued their slipping, sliding progress. The puppies were having a difficult time keeping their feet, and some wanted to desert the icy creek for the snowy banks. But Pongo was firm.

"If we leave tracks, we're done for," he said. They went on into the night.

DOGS IN BLACK SUITS

It began to snow, and at last Pongo decided that it was safe to abandon the slippery ice and strike across country. Perdita still led the line of marching puppies, and Pongo counted them as they trudged on past . . . Ninety-nine! Where was Lucky? Pongo retraced his steps to find the puppy.

"I'm tired," wailed Lucky, "and I'm hungry, and my tail's froze. And my nose is froze, and my toes are froze."

Pongo picked him up by the collar and hurried after the others. He was worried, for the snow was coming down faster and he was afraid they had lost their way. Then he heard a short bark, and a magnificent collie appeared through the swirling snow flakes.

"Pongo! Pongo!" he called. "Thank goodness. We had just about lost hope. We have shelter for you at the dairy barn across the way."

They followed the collie through a fence and up a hill into the warmth of the barn. Pleasant-faced, brown-eyed cows gazed in astonishment at them.

"Just look, Queenie," said one. "Have you ever seen so many adorable puppies? Poor dears! They're completely worn out and half frozen."

Some of the puppies started to whimper. After all, they were small and they'd come a long way through cold and snow. Also, they had had nothing to eat for hours. "I'm hungry, mother," said one to Perdita.

"I'm sorry, children . . ." Perdita started to say, when one of the cows interrupted her: "Wouldn't your children like some warm fresh milk?" she said.

"Oh, thank you," said Perdita gratefully. Soon each hungry pup had been fed. Then one by one, the puppies dropped off to sleep. The collie brought scraps of food for the weary Pongo and Perdita.

"Not much, but it might hold you as far as Dinsford. There's a Labrador there. His pet is a grocer. I'll head you that way in the morning."

While the weary Dalmatians slept, the collie stood guard. In the morning, greatly refreshed, the Pongos thanked their generous hosts, and went on their way. The storm had ended, and the countryside was now covered with a new blanket of gleaming snow. Pongo knew that their tracks would show plainly in the snow. He headed the army of pups towards the wooded countryside, where they would be better hidden.

Still, occasionally they had to cross a road, and Pongo would look searchingly up and down its length before sending the puppies across. Once they were safely on the other side, Pongo would draw a broken branch back and forth over the road to wipe out the tell-tale tracks.

The prints of one little puppy's feet do not leave marks too noticeable in fresh-fallen snow. But multiply those prints by ninety-nine, add the larger prints of two grown dogs, and you have a track difficult to erase. Pongo was trying to obliterate their tracks across a snowy road when a speeding red and black car loomed into view.

It was Cruella De Vil, who had now entered the chase, and was being closely followed by the Baduns in their rickety truck. The dogs had fled, but Cruella spotted the tracks across the road and the car screeched to a stop.

"Well, now," she exulted. "What have we

here! So they thought they could outwit Cruella! Ha! Ha!" Turning to the Baduns' truck she shouted: "Jasper! Horace! Here are their tracks, heading straight for the village. Work your way south on the side roads. I'll take the main road. See you in Dinsford." With a clashing and grinding of gears, the two machines drove off.

Pongo, Perdita and the puppies were running as fast as they could toward the sound of distant barking. It came from the Dinsford Labrador, who came racing up with excellent news.

"Pongo," he barked. "I've got a ride home for all of you, if we can make it. Come on. We'd better hurry!"

The black Labrador led them through back ways into a deserted blacksmith shop. "It's dark in here," whispered one pup. "And scary!" added another. "And it's dirty!" said a third. But, temporarily, it was shelter and a hiding place. The Labrador nodded toward a broken window.

"See that van down the street?" he said. "It's going to London as soon as the engine's repaired. And there's room for all of you."

As the three looked through the broken pane, a long red and black car flashed into the street and skidded to a stop.

"Pongo, look!" said Perdita. "There's Cruella!"

"Yes," said Pongo, "and here come Horace and Jasper." The Baduns' truck clanked to a shuddery stop. Impatiently, Cruella sat in her car while Horace and Jasper emerged and began searching the small village street.

"How will we ever get to the van?" said Perdita.

"I don't know, Perdy," answered Pongo. "But—somehow—we've got to."

Cruella De Vil, impatient at the delay in finding the Dalmatians, drove slowly up and down the street to carry on her own search. The Baduns were still combing alleys for signs of the dogs, and might return at any moment. How was Pongo to get his swarm of puppies into the van? As he pondered on the problem, two of the puppies tumbled out of the fireplace.

"Mother! Dad!" cried one. "Patch pushed me into the soot."

"Lucky pushed me first," said Patch. Both puppies were half-covered with coal-dust and hardly recognizable. Pongo stared at them. Then he turned to Perdita: "I've got an idea!" he said. Before Perdita's amazed eyes he jumped into the fireplace and rolled about in the soot.

"Pongo! What on earth . . ." began Perdita, horrified. Then Pongo emerged from the soot cloud he'd been raising. He was as black as their friend, the Labrador.

"Look!" he cried. "I'm a *Labrador!* We'll *all* roll in the soot. We'll *all* be Labradors, and, if we travel in small groups. . . ."

Perdita was frightened, and a little dubious. Besides, she hated to spoil her gleaming white coat. "I'm afraid we can't fool Cruella," she said.

"We can try," said Pongo. "Into the soot, children!"

"You mean you want us to get dirty?" asked Lucky. The puppies couldn't believe their ears. But a nod of assent from Perdita sent them rolling and tumbling in the sooty fireplace, and a great cloud of soot rose up.

The Labrador was heartily in favor of the plan. He rather liked the idea of seeing a hundred and one black Labradors. "I'll take the first bunch of puppies to the van," he said. "Then I'll stay there and haul the rest of them aboard. You follow me with little groups."

The Pongos waited and watched apprehensively at the window as the Labrador led the first puppies to the back of the van.

"Pongo," said Perdita. "I'm so afraid."

Pongo gave her a reassuring lick. "Don't worry, Perdy. It won't be long now. Soon we'll be home."

The line of black puppies passed by Horace, who stopped and looked at them in puzzlement. He plucked at Jasper's sleeve. "Look, Jasper. Do you suppose those Dalmatians have disguised themselves?"

"Oh, yes, Horace," answered Jasper sarcastically. "That's *just* what they did! Dogs are *always* painting themselves black. You idiot!" Jasper thumped Horace soundly over the head and scrambled over the nearest fence to continue his search.

It was Pongo's turn to load more puppies aboard the van. "So far, so good," he told Perdita. "I'll go ahead with the next bunch. You follow as soon as all mine are in. The van may leave at any minute."

Pongo and the Labrador frantically loaded black puppies into the van. Cruella De Vil had returned in her big car and now was screeching at the Baduns:

"They're somewhere in this village and we're going to find them! Now—get going!" The Baduns, grumbling, continued their search, while Cruella sat in her car and fidgeted nervously. Past her came another

file of black puppies, headed by an equally black Perdita.

The van's motor had started.

"There," said the mechanic to the truck driver. "That ought to do her. At least, she'll get you back to London." It was time for haste. Perdita helped the Labrador load puppies onto the van's tailgate.

"Better get aboard, ma'am," said the Labrador as Pongo raced back toward the blacksmith shop to get the last of the puppies.

"Come on, children," cried Pongo. "Run on ahead." He felt apprehensive, for between them and the safety of the van sat Cruella, watching the puppies suspiciously.

"Keep going! Keep going!" Pongo urged the pups. It was unfortunate that just as the last one, Lucky, passed under the eaves, some melting snow fell onto his back. Dripping off, it exposed the puppy's white hide and spotted markings. Cruella's suspicions had been confirmed!

"It can't be!" she shouted. "It's impossible! Horace! Jasper! Come here!"

The Baduns came on the run, but the van was already on the move, and Pongo was bounding after it with the last pup in his mouth. Perdita, on the tailgate, urged them on. Desperately, Pongo leaped for the truck, and Perdita, with a frantic grab for his collar, pulled him and the puppy to safety.

"There they go! In the van! After them!" screeched Cruella. But the black Labrador cunningly tripped the Baduns, and, before they could disentangle themselves, the van had turned the corner and was speeding along on its way to London.

THE CHASE

The van was big and roomy, and partly filled with furniture. For the first time in days Pongo and Perdita felt secure. The van driver sped along, for it was Christmas Eve, and he was anxious to get home.

"Perdy, we made it," exulted Pongo. "Just think—we'll all be home tonight." He started to sing a cheerful song:

"Soon we'll be seeing the sights of London.
Once we're there we'll never leave.
Give three cheers, a yip and a bark,
We'll be back in Regents Park,
This jolly Christmas Eve.
London is just around the corner . . ."

Suddenly the headlights of a speeding car lit up the interior of the van.

"Pongo! It's her! Cruella!" cried Perdita. The pups, frightened by the glaring lights, dived into dresser drawers and boxes. Cruella put her foot on the gas and began to overtake the van. By maneuvering her car to left and right, she hoped to be able to force the van into the ditch.

"Hey, lady! What on earth are you trying to do?" yelled the van driver, as he fought to keep his position on the slippery road.

"You crazy woman driver! Move over!"

Pongo and Perdita, inside the jolting, swaying van, desperately tried to keep their feet. The terrified puppies were safely hidden in the furniture. They could only hold on and try to ride out this mad race.

It was Horace and Jasper who decided the issue. Speeding behind Cruella's car, they had seen her attempts to ditch the van. Jasper now decided that Fate lay in his capable hands.

"Watch, Horace," he gloated. "There's nothing to it. I'll give them a bit of a nudge . . . Ha! Ha! Ha! . . . and shove them into the ditch." Jasper urged the rickety old truck to greater speed.

"Watch out, Perdy," said Pongo, as the van, the Baduns' truck and Cruella's huge car drew closer together on the narrow slippery surface of the road.

The van driver was in no mood to be delayed. He was overdue at his home in London, and the Christmas tree was waiting to be trimmed. No wild-eyed women in big cars or men in rusty trucks were going to stop *him*.

He clung to his steering wheel and continued his lively pace to London, dodging now and then to avoid the batterings of Cruella and the Baduns. Such reckless maneuverings couldn't continue forever.

Suddenly there was a bang and a slam as the Baduns, trying to ditch the van, bumped into Cruella's car. Pieces of metal showered the roadway and the van teetered precariously. But it recovered and continued on its way. Left behind in the snowy ditch were Cruella and her villainous henchmen.

"You *fools!* You *imbeciles!* You *idiots!*" she screeched.

Horace and Jasper had reached the end of their endurance. Slowly they picked themselves out of the remains of their smashed truck, and faced Cruella with whatever dignity two such low fellows could muster.

"That's enough!" they said in unison, and started to trudge down the road.

Cruella De Vil, standing in the wreckage of her expensive car, looked at the damage she had caused. Her arrogant shoulders fell and her once-proud features were twisted with tearful rage. Cruella De Vil, meanest girl in London, had given up.

HOME FOR CHRISTMAS

It was Christmas Eve in the Radcliff's little home in Regents Park, but nobody was feeling particularly cheerful. Anita was bravely putting the last touches on the Christmas tree, and Roger was listening moodily to the radio. To the accompaniment of a famous orchestra, someone was singing Roger's hit tune:

"At first you think Cruella is a devil,
But after time has worn away the shock,

You come to realize
You've seen her kind of eyes
Watching you from underneath a rock.
Cruella De Vil. . . .
Cruella De Vil. . . ."

Snap! Roger had turned off the set. Anita looked up from where she knelt by the tree.

"Don't you want to listen, Roger? After all, it *is* your first big song hit."

"I know," said Roger gloomily. He walked over to a photograph of Pongo and Perdita, and looked at it for a long time. Anita came and stood silently by his side. "I still can't believe it, Anita," he said. " . . . that Pongo and Perdita would run away."

"Here's a bit of Christmas cheer for you," said Nanny Cook, bustling in from the kitchen with a tray. Then she saw them looking at the picture. "Oh, the dear little puppies . . . sniff . . . sometimes at night I can hear them barking. But it always turns out I'm dreaming."

Dabbing her apron to her eyes, Nanny turned to go back to the kitchen. Suddenly there came a loud barking at the front door. Nanny stood stock still, then she whirled about, and, almost knocking Roger over in her mad dash past him, ran down the tiny hall and opened the door.

An avalanche of black, happy, barking dogs swarmed over Nanny as she opened the door. Knocked off her feet, the little maid lay there while some of the dogs licked her face and pranced about with glee. The rest of the canine throng streamed into the living room.

Roger was completely overpowered by the wave of happy animals, and Anita was pushed to the sofa by two of the largest.

She wasn't frightened, but she *was* a little startled.

"Roger," she cried. "What on earth . . . ?"

Roger tried to regain his feet. "Why—they're Labradors," he said.

"No—no!" cried Nanny happily, as she came running into the room. "They're Dalmatians covered with soot! Look!" She picked up a black-and-white spotted pup from the mass on the floor. "Look, here's Lucky!"

"Oh, Pongo boy—is that you?" said Roger. He pulled a handkerchief from his pocket and dabbed at the big dog's head. The soot came off, and there stood Pongo, familiar in his handsome white coat and black spots.

"Pongo! It's Pongo!" sang Roger. He grasped Pongo's paws and the two did a joyful dance around the room.

Anita, almost smothered by fond licking on her face and hands, was trying to wipe soot off the other big dog. "Perdy—oh, Perdy, my darling. You've come back!"

Nanny Cook was busy with her feather duster. "And Patch," she said, as another familiar puppy emerged from his sooty coat. "And Rolly and Penny and Freckles—oh, ho, ho! They're all here, the little dears!"

Roger hugged Anita close to him. "It's a miracle," he said.

"Yes," smiled Anita. "Oh, Rog—what a wonderful Christmas present."

Pongo and Perdita looked at each other happily. They—and the puppies—were home at last.

A DALMATIAN PLANTATION

Nanny Cook continued to wield her feather duster. Clouds of soot filled the room, and dozens of coughing, spluttering, dusty, but unmistakably black and white, spotted puppies emerged. Nanny turned to the Radcliffs, who were still happily absorbed in their own cluster of dogs.

"Did you notice," she said, "there are a lot more of them."

Roger and Anita looked. And then they blinked in utter disbelief. The room was literally overflowing with puppies—dozens and dozens of Dalmatian puppies!

They crowded on the top of the piano, spilled over onto the keyboard, and from there onto the bench. The window seat was full of them, and so were all the chairs. The coffee table was covered.

Dalmatian pups swarmed over the sofa. Puppies thronged the hall. A few had found their way to the fireplace mantel to avoid the crowd on the floor. And all the way up the stairs to the second floor landing, puppies sat patiently waiting while Nanny Cook as patiently dusted.

"Look, Anita," exclaimed Roger. "Puppies everywhere. There must be a hundred!"

Nanny was dusting and counting: "One, two, three, and four is seven . . ." Roger and Anita joined in. "Two, four, six . . . and three makes nine more."

Eleven puppies were discovered under the curtains by the window, and Anita found quite a number under the Christmas tree.

A closer search revealed one in the fireplace, and finally Roger said, "Let's see now. That's eighty-four! Add our *fifteen* puppies, plus Pongo and Perdita . . . and we have ONE HUNDRED AND ONE DALMATIANS! Oh, ho, Pongo . . . what an old rascal you are!" He rubbed the big dog's head. "Where did they all come from?"

Anita sank onto the sofa. "What will we do with all of them?" she said.

Nanny had finished dusting the last puppy. She turned now to hear what Roger would say. Pongo and Perdita looked at each other apprehensively. The puppies looked at Roger, and tremblingly awaited his answer.

Roger looked at the floor.

Finally he looked up, to meet the gaze of one hundred and one pairs of anxious eyes. Roger smiled—a big, warm, happy smile. "We'll *keep* them," he said simply.

Pongo and Perdita sighed with relief. The warm hearts of their human pets hadn't disappointed them. The puppies wriggled and barked and wagged their tails.

"Keep all one hundred and one—in this little house?" gasped Anita, over the din.

"We'll buy a big place in the country," answered Roger. "We'll have a *plantation*—er —a *Dalmatian plantation.*"

"Oh, Roger," smiled Anita. She hugged him and added, "That's truly an inspiration."

"It'll be a sensation!" laughed Nanny, and turned to dust one puppy that she somehow had missed.

Roger picked his way through the happy, squirming dogs to the piano and began to improvise:

"We'll have a Dalmatian plantation—
  a Dalmatian plantation, I say.
A life-long vacation . . .
  complete resignation
To sweet relaxation and play.
Our new population is no complication . . ."

Anita interrupted: "And we do have enough money."

"No, no!" said Roger. "Remuneration!" He finished the song:

"We'll have a Dalmatian plantation,
Where our population can roam.
In this location, our whole aggregation
Will love our plantation home."

And if you ever go to a certain place in England, you can still see those dogs today, in their plantation home, happily roaming its woods and fields—the one hundred and one Dalmatians.

PETER PAN

In a quiet street in London lived the Darling family. There were Father and Mother Darling, and Wendy, Michael, and John. There was also the children's nursemaid, Nana—a St. Bernard dog.

For Nana and the children the best hour of the day was bedtime, for then they were together in the nursery. There Wendy told wonderful stories about Peter Pan of Never Land. This Never Land was a magical spot with Indians and Mermaids and Fairies—and wicked pirates, too.

John and Michael liked best of all to play pirate. They had some fine, slashing duels between Peter Pan and his arch-enemy, the Pirate Captain Hook.

Father Darling did not like this kind of play. He blamed it on Wendy's stories of Peter Pan, and Father Darling did not approve of those stories, either.

"It is time for Wendy to grow up," he decided. "This is your last night in the nursery, Wendy girl."

All the children were much upset at that. Without Wendy in the nursery there would be no more stories of Peter Pan! Then to make matters worse, Father Darling became annoyed with Nana and decided the children were too old to be treated like puppies. So he tied Nana in the garden for the night.

When Mother and Father Darling had gone out for the evening, leaving the children snug in their beds with Nana on guard below, who should come to the nursery but Peter Pan! It seemed he had been flying in from Never Land to listen to the bedtime stories, all unseen. Only Nana had caught sight of him once and nipped off his shadow as he escaped. So back he came, looking for his lost shadow and hoping for a story about himself. With him was a fairy, Tinker Bell. When Peter heard that Wendy was to be moved from the nursery, he hit upon a plan. "I'll take you to Never Land with me, to tell stories to my Lost Boys!" he decided as Wendy sewed his shadow back on.

Wendy thought that was a lovely idea—if Michael and John could go, too. So Peter

Pan taught them all to fly—with happy thoughts and faith and trust, and a sprinkling of Tinker Bell's pixie dust. Then out the nursery window they sailed, heading for Never Land, while Nana barked frantically below.

Back in Never Land, on the pirate ship, Captain Hook was as usual grumbling about Peter Pan. You see, once in a fair fight long

ago Peter Pan had cut off one of the pirate captain's hands, so that he had to wear a hook instead. Then Pan threw the hand to a crocodile, who enjoyed the taste of Hook so much that he had been lurking around ever since hoping to nibble at the rest of him.

Fortunately for the pirate, the crocodile had also swallowed a clock which went "tick tock" when he came near and warned Captain Hook.

Now, as Captain Hook grumbled about his young enemy, there was a call from the crow's nest.

"Peter Pan ahoy!"

"What? Where?" shouted Hook, twirling his spy-glass around the sky. And then he spied Peter and the children, pausing for a rest on a cloud. "Swoggle me eyes, it *is* Pan!" Hook gloated. "Pipe up the crew. . . . Man the guns. . . . We'll get him this time at last!"

"Oh, Peter, it's just as I've dreamed it would be—Mermaid Lagoon and all," Wendy was saying when the first of the pirates' cannonballs ripped through the cloud close beside their feet and went sizzling on past.

"Look out!" cried Peter Pan. "Tinker Bell, take Wendy and the boys to the island. I'll stay here and draw Hook's fire!"

Away flew Tinker Bell, as fast as she could go. In her naughty little heart she hoped the children would fall behind and be lost. Especially was she jealous of the Wendy girl who seemed to have won Peter Pan's heart.

Straight through the Never Land jungle Tink flew, down into a clearing beside an old dead tree called Hangman's Tree. She landed on a toadstool, bounced to a shiny leaf, and pop! a secret door opened for her in the knot of the hollow tree.

Zip! Down a slippery tunnel Tink slid. She landed at the bottom in an underground room—the secret house of Peter Pan.

Ting-a-ling! she tinkled, flitting about from one corner of the room to the next. She was

trying to awaken the sleeping Lost Boys, who lay like so many curled-up balls of fur.

At last, rather grumpily, they woke up and stretched in their little fur suits. And they listened to Tinker Bell.

"What? Pan wants us to shoot down a terrible Wendy bird? Lead us to it!" they shouted, and out they hurried.

When Wendy and Michael and John appeared, flying wearily, the Lost Boys tried to pelt them with stones and sticks—especially the "Wendy bird." Down tumbled Wendy, all her happy thoughts destroyed—for without them no one can fly.

"Hurray! We got the Wendy bird!" the Lost Boys shouted.

But then Peter Pan arrived. How angry he was when he discovered that the boys had tried to shoot down Wendy, even though he had caught her before she could be hurt.

"I brought her to be a mother to us all and to tell us stories," said Peter.

"Come on, Wendy," he went on. "I'll show you the Mermaids. Boys, take Michael and John to hunt some Indians."

So Peter and Wendy flew away, and the boys marched off through the forest, planning to capture some Indians. There were wild animals all around, but the boys never thought to be afraid, and not a creature harmed them as through the woods they went.

"First we'll surround the Indians," John decided. "Then we'll take them by surprise."

John's plan worked splendidly, but it was the Indians who used it. Disguised as moving trees, they quietly surrounded the boys and took *them* by surprise!

Soon, bound with ropes, the row of boys marched away, led by the Indians to their village on the cliff.

"Don't worry, the Indians are our friends," the Lost Boys said, but the chief looked very stern.

Meanwhile, on the other side of the island, Wendy and Peter were visiting the Mermaids in their peaceful Mermaid Lagoon. As they were chatting together, Peter suddenly said, "Hush!"

A boat from the pirate ship was going by. In it were wicked Captain Hook and Smee, the pirate cook. And at the stern, all bound with ropes, sat Princess Tiger Lily, daughter of the Indian chief.

"We'll make her talk," sneered Captain Hook.

"She'll tell us where Peter Pan lives, or we'll leave her tied to slippery Skull Rock, where the tide will wash over her."

But proud and loyal Tiger Lily would not say a single word.

Peter and Wendy flew to Skull Rock. Peter, by imitating Hook's voice, tried to trick Smee into setting Tiger Lily free. That almost worked, but Hook discovered the trick, and came after Peter with his sword. Then what a thrilling duel they had, all over that rocky cave where Princess Tiger Lily sat, with the tide up to her chin!

Peter won the duel and rescued Tiger Lily just in the nick of time. Then away he flew to the Indian village, to see that the princess arrived safely home. And Wendy came along behind.

When Peter and Wendy brought Tiger Lily home, the chief set the captives all free. Then what a wonderful feast they had! All the boys did Indian dances and learned wild Indian chants, and Peter Pan was made a chief! Only Wendy had no fun at all, for she had to help the squaws carry firewood.

"I've had enough of Never Land," she thought grumpily. "I'm ready to go home right now!"

While the Indian celebration was at its height, Smee the pirate crept up through the underbrush and captured Tinker Bell.

Trapped in his cap, she struggled and kicked, but Smee took her back to the pirate ship and presented her to Captain Hook.

"Ah, Miss Bell," said Hook sympathetically, "I've heard how badly Peter Pan has treated you since that scheming girl Wendy came. How nice it would be if we could kidnap her and take her off to sea to scrub the decks and cook for the pirate crew!"

Tink tinkled happily at the thought.

"But, alas," sighed Hook, "we don't know where Pan's house is, so we cannot get rid of Wendy for you."

Tink thought this over. "You won't hurt Peter?" she asked, in solemn tinkling tones.

"Of course not!" promised Hook.

Then she marched to a map of Never Land and traced a path to Peter's hidden house.

"Thank you, my dear," said wicked Captain Hook, and he locked her up in a lantern cage, while he went off to capture Peter Pan!

That night when Wendy tucked the children into their beds in the underground house, she talked to them about home and mother. Soon they were all so homesick that they wanted to leave at once for home. Wendy invited all the Lost Boys to come and live with the Darling family. Only Peter refused to go. He simply looked the other way as Wendy and the boys told him good-bye and climbed the tunnel to Hangman's Tree.

Up in the woods near Hangman's Tree waited Hook and his pirate band. As each boy came out, a hand was clapped over his mouth and he was quickly tied up with ropes. Last of all came Wendy. Zip, zip, she was bound up too, and the crew marched off with their load of children, back to the pirate ship.

"Blast it!" muttered Hook. "We still don't have Pan!"

So he and Smee left a wicked bomb, wrapped as a gift from Wendy, for poor Peter to find. Very soon, they hoped, Peter would open it and blow himself straight out of Never Land.

Imagine how terrible Tinker Bell felt when she saw all the children prisoners, and knew it was her fault!

The boys were given the terrible choice between turning pirates and walking the

plank. To the boys the life of a pirate sounded fine, sad to say, and they were all ready to join up. But Wendy was shocked at that. "Never!" she cried.

"Very well," said Hook. "Then you shall be the first to walk the plank, my dear."

Everyone felt so terrible—though Wendy was ever so brave—that no one noticed when Tinker Bell escaped and flew off to warn Peter Pan.

What a dreadful moment when Wendy said good-bye and bravely walked out the long narrow plank that led to the churning sea!

And then she disappeared. Everyone listened, breathless, waiting for a splash, but not a sign of one came! What could the silence mean?

Then they heard a familiar, happy crow. It was Pan in the rigging, high above. Warned by Tinker Bell, he had escaped just in time to scoop up Wendy in mid-air and fly with her to safety.

"This time you have gone too far, Hook," Peter cried.

He swooped down from the rigging, all set for a duel. And what a duel it was!

While they fought, Tinker Bell slashed the ropes that bound the boys and they beat the pirates into jumping overboard and rowing away in their boat. Then Peter knocked Hook's sword overboard, and Hook jumped, too. When the children saw the wicked Captain Hook, he was swimming for the boat, with the crocodile tick-tocking hungrily behind him.

Peter Pan took command of the pirate ship. "Heave those halyards. Up with the jib. We're sailing to London," he cried.

"Oh, Michael! John!" cried Wendy. "We're going home!"

And sure enough, with happy thoughts and faith and trust, and a liberal sprinkling of pixie dust, away flew that pirate ship through the skies till the gangplank was run out to the Darlings' nursery windowsill.

But now that they had arrived, the Lost Boys did not want to stay. "We've sort of decided to stick with Pan," they said.

So Wendy, John, and Michael waved good-bye as Peter Pan's ship sailed off through the sky, taking the Lost Boys home to Never Land, where they still live today.

THE ADVENTURES OF
ROBIN HOOD

ROBIN AND MAID MARIAN

FROM THE steps of the manor house of the Earl of Huntingdon, an old steward watched the scene in the courtyard. Squires shouted orders to pages. Grooms made last-minute adjustments to girths and saddles. Men-at-arms joked as they checked their weapons.

Getting ready for war was an old story to the steward, but he never tired of it. And this time his master would be gone a long time. For the Earl was going off with the King on a crusade to the Holy Land, to try to win it back from the followers of Mohammed.

Two pages were holding the horses ready for the Earl and his daughter, Marian.

There was a sudden hush as the tall figure of the Earl appeared. He scanned the courtyard with approval.

Suddenly, an old woman came clumping down the steps, carrying a hat and veil in her hand.

"Marian!" the old woman shouted. "Marian!"

The Earl frowned. "Is our daughter not yet ready?"

"Aye, sire," the old woman bobbed her head. "She's ready this past hour, and dressed as pretty as a daffydowndilly."

"Fetch her, then!" commanded the Earl. "If we do not leave within the hour, we will miss the King at Nottingham."

The old nurse went off, muttering and clucking. At the gateway, she almost bumped into a tall grizzled man with a pair of greyhounds at his heel and a longbow over his shoulder. He was Hugh Fitzooth, the gamekeeper.

"Where's that harum-scarum son of yours?" the old nurse asked.

Hugh Fitzooth smiled. "My lad's in the meadow, drawing his bow against a willow wand. But if you're looking for the Maid

Marian, she's not with Robin this time." But Maid Marian was in the meadow with his son, though Robin was not aware of it.

In fact, Robin was aware of nothing except that, for some strange reason, he had missed his willow-wand target twice in succession. He looked again at the two arrows firmly stuck in the tree behind his target and fitted a third arrow to his bow. As he raised the bow, he caught sight of a slight movement behind a tree and the flutter of a dress.

So that was the answer. It was a simple matter of a long stick with a fork at one end and Maid Marian at the other.

It was like Maid Marian to tease him like this, even when she was about to leave on a journey. Robin rushed after her, but his foot caught on a root, and he tumbled down, head over heels, almost at her feet.

Now came Robin's chance to get even. Reaching for his bow, which had slipped from his shoulder, he started to rise from the ground. But when Marian turned to run away again, he used the bow to trip her neatly.

Just at that moment, the old nurse arrived. She began scolding at once. "Saints above! Now look at you. My Lord Earl waiting and here you are, groveling in the dirt. A girl old enough to serve the Queen is old enough to act like a lady."

Robin lifted his eyebrows. "Act like a lady! That is the last thing the Lady Marian is ever likely to do."

Marian drew herself up stiffly and surprised both the old nurse and Robin with her words.

"Inform the Earl, my dear Lord and father, that I attend him presently."

An hour later, the Earl of Huntingdon rode out from his manor house, with his daughter, the Lady Marian, at his side. It was the first stage of the long journey that would take the Earl to the Holy Land.

OFF TO THE CRUSADES

As Marian entered the great hall of Nottingham Castle with her father, she caught sight of three people who had just come out of the inner council room.

One was a tall man who wore over his armor a long white surcoat of silk, bearing the crusader's red cross on breast and shoulder. Marian knew at once he was King Richard.

Beside him stood his mother, Queen Eleanor of Aquitaine, whose lady-in-waiting

Marian hoped to be. The third member of the party was the King's brother, Prince John. Marian wondered why she should so suddenly dislike the Prince.

King Richard caught sight of her father and his face lit up. "Welcome, Huntingdon," he said.

The Earl dropped on one knee before his king.

"Now truly," continued the King, "we can say that the best and bravest men in all England are gathered here."

"God make us worthy of your trust, sire," said the Earl. He glanced at Queen Eleanor, then back to King Richard. "Sire," he said, "I have a boon to ask the Queen."

The King nodded his consent and the Earl bowed low before the proud old Queen.

"I prithee, Madam," he asked, "take this girl, my daughter, into thy care."

The Queen accepted Marian. It would be a pleasure to have at her side this young girl, daughter of the faithful Earl. Such favors were easy to grant.

But there was another favor still to come. As Queen Eleanor turned to join her sons, the Sheriff of Nottingham stepped forward.

"My Lord King," he said, "I, too, would beg a boon. My men and I would follow our king across the seas."

King Richard hesitated. These men were needed here to protect his kingdom. Yet how could he refuse their request to fight in the Holy War?

"The King wills it," he said, and saw the Sheriff's face light up with gratitude.

But these men must be replaced, and soon. That would be up to his brother, Prince John, who would rule England and keep order during his absence.

Turning to John, the King commanded, "Find a new sheriff for Nottingham, and men to serve him."

"I will, my Lord," said John.

Now the royal party moved out into the bright sunshine. As the King appeared, a mighty shout went up from the knights and men-at-arms.

"God save King Richard!"

The shouting continued as Richard went down the steps and crossed to an altar where the Archbishops of Canterbury and York waited. The crowd became quiet, and Richard spoke.

"My Lord Archbishop of Canterbury," he said, "we ask a blessing on this, our most holy enterprise."

The archbishop turned toward the army and gave the blessing.

Every eye was on Richard when the prayer ended. He drew his sword and kissed the hilt. Bright sunlight flashed on his red-gold hair.

"Advance my banner," he shouted. "God wills it!"

Like the crash of a wave, his words came back from a thousand throats. "God wills it!" It was the battle cry of the Crusades.

A trumpet blared triumphantly, then another and another. Slowly, the army of crusaders got under way. Spectators waved from the castle walls, and here and there a lady wept. Someone began to sing a marching song, and soon the whole army was singing.

Only Prince John watched the crusaders with cold impatience. When the last man had vanished and no sound of the trumpets could be heard, Prince John spoke to the man who was waiting in the shadows.

De Lacy approached, his dark, bearded face full of cunning.

"Kings have died on crusades," Prince John said to De Lacy. "The Prince who is heir to the throne needs trustworthy men about him. Is that not so?"

De Lacy's words were smooth and silky. "My Lord, I am yours as blade to hilt." For a long moment, the two men looked at each other in silence.

"You shall be my new Sheriff of Nottingham," the Prince promised. "As Sheriff, you will enforce the laws in Sherwood Forest. You will enforce them to the very letter. For such a task you will need a larger force."

"Sire," objected De Lacy, "can you support so large a force?"

Prince John had been thinking about this. "There must be new taxes, enough for an army and other things we need. I shall look to see the finest bowmen wearing the black and gold livery of the new Sheriff of Nottingham."

"A few weeks, sire, is all I need," promised De Lacy.

"Good!" exclaimed the Prince. "You shall show me what they can do at the shooting match in Nottingham Fair. Perhaps we can offer a special prize, a golden arrow, for the best marksman."

The two men stared down from the castle battlements. King Richard's army of crusaders was gone and the landscape was empty. To the two watching men, full of evil thoughts, it appeared rich and prosperous. Best of all, it was defenseless. There was no one strong enough or bold enough to challenge the new ruler of England.

THE SHOOTING MATCH

Nottingham Fair was one of the most famous in all England. Royalty and gentlefolk came from London to watch the contests. Farmers and peddlers set up stalls to sell their wares. It was a holiday for all.

The most popular event of the Fair was the shooting match. Everyone was eager to

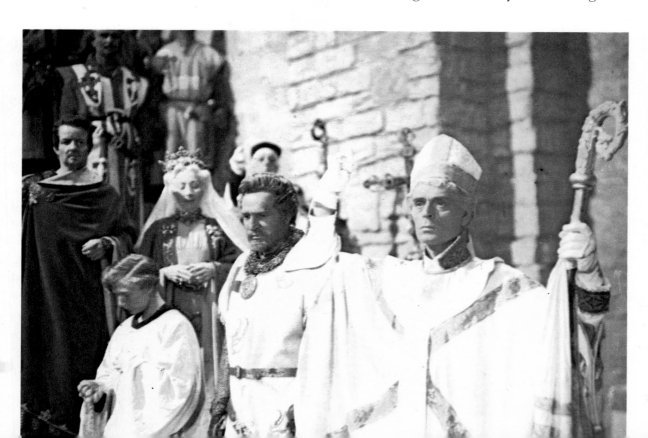

see who would win the prize, a golden arrow.

Through the crowds wandered the merry minstrel, Allan-a-Dale, plucking his battered lute. With a joke here, a song there, he greeted old friends and looked for new ones. His keen eyes missed nothing.

Suddenly he caught sight of a group of archers whose dress marked them as independent men. He drew closer and sang softly:

"Beware, O ye archers of Nottingham
Fair,
Of our new Sheriff's hirelings, beware—
O.
Since they levy a tax on thy chattels else-
where,
They may here tax thy bow and thine
arrow."

The archers laughed at the minstrel's sly song, and one of them pointed to Robin and his father.

"We're counting on Fitzooth and his lad to outshoot the Sheriff's men!"

Robin and his father both smiled at this boast, but they knew it would not be easy to win the match.

By the time the match was half over, the odds were in favor of the Sheriff's men. One by one, the independent archers dropped out, until only the two Fitzooths remained.

In the Royal Box, halfway down the range, Prince John was as pleased with De Lacy as the Sheriff was pleased with himself. One of De Lacy's men was certain to win the shooting match.

Shouts of applause rose again as the men shot another round. This time, three men, all wearing the Sheriff's black and gold livery, drifted away to the benches where the other defeated bowmen sat. Now the odds had swung in favor of the independent archers.

The marker was calling the score in ringing tones. "These are the three remaining archers: Red Gill, in the service of the Sheriff of Nottingham . . ." Applause died away quickly.

"Robin Fitzooth of Huntingdon," the marker said, pausing as a roar of applause drowned his voice, "and Hugh Fitzooth of Huntingdon." The cheer that followed was loudest and longest.

Prince John turned to De Lacy and said, "The crowd is not cheering your bowman, De Lacy."

"My men have been gathering the new taxes, my Lord. What can you expect?"

Prince John looked thoughtful. "Your men need not be liked," he admitted.

The Sheriff was confident. "Red Gill will win for us."

The marker's voice came again. "The final match will be shot at a distance of six score yards." The crowd gasped at the distance.

Red Gill was first to shoot at the distant target. Straight and true, the arrow went whirring through the air. The crowd saw that it had pierced the target, cutting the edge of the inner circle.

Now it was Robin's turn. He raised his bow, aimed quickly, and shot. It was more important than ever to beat the Sheriff's bully.

The roar of the crowd was deafening, and Robin knew he must have succeeded. Yes, there was his arrow, in the dead center of the inner circle.

Robin could not resist a mocking glance at Red Gill, whose thoughts were grim as he withdrew into the crowd.

But the shooting match was not yet over. Hugh Fitzooth had not had his final turn. Without hurry he put his toe to the mark, and let fly. Hugh's arrow split Robin's down the middle. It was another perfect shot.

There was a second of stunned silence, followed by thunderous applause. Robin thumped his father on the back. In the Royal Box, De Lacy could not meet Prince John's furious glance.

Now it was time for the Queen to award the prize. The cheers died away as she leaned forward in the Royal Box, the golden arrow in her hand.

"Good bowman," said the Queen to Hugh Fitzooth, "step forward."

Hugh bowed. "My Lady Paramount," he said, "I beg a favor. Let the golden arrow be given to him whose arrow hit the mark first, and no less truly than mine."

"Well said, yeoman," the Queen smiled her approval, and beckoned to Robin.

For a moment Robin hesitated, then came forward to accept the prize. As he bowed and thanked the Queen, his eyes met the mischievous glance of Lady Marian, sitting nearby.

Bowing again in front of Marian, he offered the golden arrow to her.

"Thank you, Robin. It will remind me of this day, wherever I may go," she said.

Queen Eleanor rose and Marian hurried to attend her. As the royal guests passed through the crowds, Prince John beckoned to De Lacy and whispered in his ear.

ROBIN BECOMES
AN OUTLAW

The independent archers had watched the award of the golden arrow to Robin with great satisfaction. But the Sheriff was not going to let these men get away from him. As they moved with the crowds to leave the Fair, De Lacy's voice stopped them.

"Hear me, good yeomen!" the Sheriff called out, as confident and sure of himself as if Red Gill had won. "Would you eat and drink of the best? Then, hear ye! Every man who hit the inner circle at four score yards is invited to take service with me."

A few men moved away from the others. The rest stood undecided, watching Hugh Fitzooth. Then they saw him turn away.

Even this did not stop the Sheriff. "What say you, good Fitzooth?" he asked. "Will you and your son change your coats?"

Hugh Fitzooth turned slowly to face the Sheriff. "In the old days," said Fitzooth, "I'd ha' been proud to wear the King's livery. But a forester in Sherwood nowadays is no better than a tax gatherer and a bully."

"Silence!" roared De Lacy.

"Nay," said Fitzooth. "It is time an honest man spoke out." He glared his defiance at the angry Sheriff and strode away. Most of the independent archers followed him.

The Sheriff watched them go, then turned and smiled crookedly at Red Gill. "What do you do," he asked, nodding toward the departing figure of Fitzooth, "when the cock crows too loudly?"

"Trim his comb, of course."

"Of course," repeated the Sheriff, and waved his hand in dismissal. No further words were necessary as Red Gill turned away and followed Hugh Fitzooth and Robin at a safe distance.

Meanwhile, Robin and his father trudged on. Soon they left Nottingham far behind and reached the edge of Sherwood Forest.

Father and son continued their journey, going ever deeper into the forest. Giant beech trees made a huge canopy over their heads and the sunlight flickered through the leaves.

" 'Tis a fair forest," Robin said.

Hugh Fitzooth nodded. "Aye, 'tis fair indeed. Yet Sherwood was a better forest when our bonny King was here."

Even as he spoke these words, he straightened up violently, choked, and then pitched forward on his face.

Robin stood still, gaping at the arrow in his father's back. Then, another arrow flew through the air. Quickly Robin dived for cover behind a tree.

While he waited, hoping that the murderer would show himself, a third arrow flew by. Now in a shaft of sunlight that came through the trees, Robin saw the colors of the murderer's livery. They were black and yellow.

"One of the Sheriff's cut-throats," thought Robin, and knew he could expect no mercy. It was a man's wits against a boy's. Just in time, Robin threw himself to the earth as Red Gill's arrow sang harmlessly overhead.

Before Red Gill could recover, Robin was on his feet and had let fly his shaft. It thudded into Red Gill's chest. For a long minute the huge man swayed unsteadily. Then he crashed to the ground.

Now Robin's quick ears caught the sound of hoofbeats. Straightening up, he began to run, dodging from bush to bush. Before darkness came, Robin was safely hidden in a cave, far in the depths of Sherwood Forest.

As the months went by, other men who had trouble with the Sheriff joined Robin in the forest. Stories about them were whispered from one person to another, until the minstrel, Allan-a-Dale, heard about them. His bright eyes and sharp ears were always alert for news, and he enjoyed making up new songs about the things he saw and heard.

One morning he came into Nottingham Square, singing as cheerfully as ever.

There were not too many people about so early in the morning, but Allan-a-Dale saw a small group of idle folk outside the inn.

Wandering closer to them, he struck a chord on his lute and began to sing:

"Now Robin who was called Fitzooth
Is dwelling in the wood;
His coat is changed to Lincoln green,
His name is Robin Hood."

The townsmen looked up with interest as the minstrel began a second verse:

"Oh, Robin Hood doth hunt the deer,
That in the woodlands prance,
But oft times shoots the Sheriff's men
By sorrowful mischance."

"He has good cause," someone growled. " 'Tis well known who killed his father."

Allan-a-Dale nodded. He was about to start on the third stanza of his new ballad when he was drowned out by the harsh notes of a trumpet.

One of the Royal Foresters, a small man with an evil face, was standing beside a bulletin post at the foot of the church steps.

"Harken! Harken!" he shouted as the townsfolk in the square drifted curiously toward him. Waving a sheet of parchment in the air, he began to recite:

"Having been informed of the felonies, robberies, and murders committed by the man known as Robin Hood, our Liege Lord, Prince John, hereby pronounces upon Robin Hood sentence of outlawry!"

Allan-a-Dale was quick to seize on this latest bit of news and add a new verse to his ballad.

"Oh, Robin Hood, poor Robin Hood,
With a riddle de diddle de day . . .
He robs the rich to help the poor,
A most unusual practice,
And now that he has been outlawed
He needn't pay his taxes."

TAXES, TAXES, TAXES

In the dreadful days that followed, the Sheriff's men were kept busy collecting taxes. There were times when it seemed that nothing that crawled, flew, swam, or walked in England could escape being taxed.

The people groaned and paid, and groaned and paid again. They had no other choice. But some, like William Scathelock, could not remain silent. He had already paid one tax when the Sheriff's men came to collect a second time.

When they drove off his herd of goats, he clenched his fists and tried to choke back his rage. When they threw his son brutally to the ground, he became dangerously angry.

Just when he felt he could stand no more, De Lacy came cantering up and stared at the angry man. Then he asked, "Would you keep your cattle and go free of the tax?"

Eagerly Scathelock caught hold of the Sheriff's stirrup leathers and knelt down. "Show me how, sire," he begged.

De Lacy's smile was thin and cold. "Report has it," he said, "that you know where the outlaw Robin Hood is hiding. Lead us to him, and our reward will pay your tax thrice over."

Scathelock rose to his feet and folded his arms across his chest. There was no doubt of his meaning.

De Lacy wheeled his horse around. "Bring him along," he commanded, and two men jumped to do his bidding.

The Sheriff put spurs to his horse and galloped off down the road that skirted the forest. He was so angry at Scathelock that he did not notice where he was going. He nearly knocked down a palmer, a pilgrim who wore two crossed palm leaves to show that he had been in the Holy Land.

Just beyond, another group of his foresters were dragging a prisoner toward him. After them came a forester with a dead deer.

"Another poacher who has been hunting on land forbidden to him?" De Lacy asked the leader of the bowmen.

"Caught red-handed, sire, shooting the king's fallow deer," the man boasted.

"I had no other meat," the poacher explained. "To pay my taxes, I sold my cattle."

"Always the same excuse," said the Sheriff. "Bring me the hide to Nottingham and this poacher with it." With a wave of his hand, De Lacy galloped off toward Nottingham.

No sooner were the Sheriff's men out of sight than the palmer, who had nearly been knocked down by De Lacy's galloping horse, stepped out of the forest. This man was really Robin Hood.

Turning back to the forest, Robin followed a path until he reached a hollow tree. From the tree he took a longbow and a quiver full of arrows. The arrows were bright red and curiously made. Below the steel tip, the round head of the arrow was pierced with holes. Fitting one of these arrows to his bow, Robin fired it high into the air.

As the arrow gathered speed, the air rushed through the holes in the round head, making the arrow scream. From all directions, Robin Hood's men came running at the whistle of the signal arrow. Will Scarlet, who was in charge while Robin Hood was away, glanced at it quickly, then turned to the rest of the outlaw band.

"Off with your kirtles and on with your rags," he rapped out. "There's need for beggars in Nottingham Square."

Outside the Sheriff's house in Nottingham Square, a crowd had gathered. The people were curious to see what would happen to the two men who had dared to defy the Sheriff's authority.

The prisoners showed no fear, in spite of the Sheriff's plans to torture them. Scathelock was held hand and foot in the stocks, unable to move. His face was without expression as two foresters passed, carrying a burning brazier.

Will Stutely, the poacher, was equally helpless. Wrapped in the skin of the deer he had killed, he had been tied round the waist with a long rope. The rope, in turn, ran through a pulley attached to a beam which jutted out from the Sheriff's house.

There was a murmur from the crowd when De Lacy appeared. He looked around

the square and seemed to be satisfied. Gazing down at Stutely, he gave a curt order. "Hoist him up!"

The foresters heaved on the rope and hauled the helpless man up into the air, where he swung to and fro. A growl of protest from the crowd was silenced.

When he was ready, De Lacy nodded to the foresters with the brazier, who set it directly beneath Stutely's head. The stinging smoke rose in a heavy cloud, tearing at Stutely's eyes and throat.

The Sheriff watched with a cruel smile, enjoying the man's sufferings.

Then he turned toward the opposite end of the square, where five horsemen were waiting, armed with quarter-staves. Before he gave them their signal, De Lacy faced the crowd. "Let this be a warning to evildoers," he shouted.

The first horseman, holding his quarterstaff like a lance, galloped toward Stutely. His staff struck the poacher and set him swinging like a pendulum. The second horseman thundered after his leader, his thick staff raised. As he came level with Stutely, he brought the weapon down savagely on his back.

Scathelock, who had his back to the torture, twisted desperately to see what was going on. Out of the corner of his eye, he saw a third horseman ride past and strike fiercely at Stutely.

"Shame!" roared Scathelock.

A forester struck him across the face with a heavy chain and Scathelock slumped down, unconscious. But his cry had roused the crowd. Each attack on Stutely by the circling riders was greeted by howls of "Shame!"

At the rear of the crowd, a palmer in a long black cloak turned away as though unable to bear the sight. With him went several beggars.

Together, they drifted toward the empty stalls, behind which the horsemen galloped as they circled for another attack on Stutely.

Quietly, the little group of ragged men crouched down and waited for the next horseman. As he approached, the palmer threw aside his cloak and stood revealed as Robin Hood. Before the horseman could grasp what was happening, Robin caught the man by the left leg and heaved upwards. The astonished rider shot out of the saddle.

Robin swung himself onto the horse's back and rode out into the square. Meanwhile, the second and third horsemen were being unsaddled and replaced by two other members of his band, Will Scarlet and Cobly.

One group of Robin Hood's men rescued Scathelock from the stocks. Robin himself freed Stutely, while others made sure that none of the Sheriff's men would be able to find their horses in time to follow the outlaws.

From the steps of his house, De Lacy watched the outlaws disappear, his face white with fury. The crowd, aroused at last, showed their contempt by pelting him with farm produce from the stalls.

"Drive the mob out of the square!" he commanded. The foresters plunged into the crowd, striking right and left with their spears and quarterstaves. But the townfolk exchanged blow for blow.

The battle raged until Prince John came riding up. As soon as he appeared, the crowd melted away. Grimly, the Prince dismounted.

"Where is this force of a hundred new foresters you've been boasting about?" he demanded.

"Throughout the countryside," the Sheriff replied smoothly, "gathering taxes for the Royal Treasury."

The Prince's anger could not be turned aside so easily. "Meanwhile," he said, "a handful of ragged outlaws dares to enter Nottingham in broad daylight."

"My Lord," he said, "I have been guilty of holding this Robin Hood too lightly. On the morrow, I myself will lead a full force against him. Before I return, I will rid Sherwood Forest of this outlaw . . . and every last one of his band. . . ."

JOHN LITTLE CHANGES HIS NAME

Robin Hood was up early next morning. When he came out of the cave in which he slept, he saw Scathelock and Stutely, the two new members of his band. They were standing kneedeep in the pool below the waterfall.

Scathelock wore a clean bandage across his face, and the morning sun showed up the full horror of Stutely's tortured back.

As Robin moved quietly past, Scathelock took up a handful of coarse salt. "This will hurt," he said, "but it will heal." He rubbed the salt into the welts and bruises on Stutely's back. Stutely gritted his teeth against the pain.

Robin watched the man's courage with admiration. "I'd bellow like a bull calf if you did that to me," he said.

Robin had scarcely finished his own morning wash when he heard the scream of a signal arrow.

Robin picked up the arrow, glanced at it, and handed it to Will Scarlet.

Stutely joined them. "What does that mean?" he asked.

Scarlet explained. "This arrow means that there is someone in the neighborhood who may be friend or enemy. We'll go with you, Robin."

Robin tapped the horn at his belt. "Nay, Cousin Will. If I have need of you, I'll call."

It was not long before he saw the reason for the signal arrow. At the foot of a hill ran a fairly broad stream, and on the other side of this a man was walking. He was a tremendous man, very tall and very broad, and he was heading for a tiny footbridge.

Robin kept out of sight until the man reached the footbridge. Then he stepped forward. "Stand aside, fellow!"

"Why?" the stranger asked quietly.

"To let the better man pass."

The stranger thought this over. "Then you stand aside," he suggested.

Robin took an arrow from his quiver.

"Were you as tall as your pride, Goliath," he said, "this would bring you down."

The stranger looked from the arrow to Robin. "An arrow against a staff is not a man's game," he said.

Robin flushed and lowered his bow. "No man ever named me coward. Will you wait while I cut a staff?"

The stranger chuckled. "Aye."

He leaned forward on his staff while Robin lopped off a sapling of ash with his short sword. When the balance satisfied him, he returned to the bridge.

The big man raised his staff. "Come on, little David," he said. For the next few minutes, they struck and parried with no special advantage to either.

Robin made the first scoring blow. He ducked a tremendous swipe from the stranger and, while the man was off-balance, whipped in a shrewd blow to the ribs. The stranger stepped back, parried Robin's next blow, and paused.

"Well done, lad," he said. "I'll pay you back if I can."

He attacked with a flurry of blows, so that Robin had all he could do to defend himself. Then the stranger seemed to grow tired. He stepped back a pace or two, and Robin moved in close.

Like lightning, the stranger's staff flashed out and Robin took a resounding thwack on the skull. Too late he realized that he had been tricked. He lost his balance, clutched

wildly at the air, and went over backwards into the river. When he bobbed to the surface, shaking the water from his eyes, the big man held out his staff and pulled him to shore. The two men, big and little, grinned at each other.

"Beat me with bowstrings," Robin said when he could catch his breath, "if I ever dispute any more bridges with you. You've cracked my head, and drowned my hunting horn."

He took the hunting horn from his belt and shook the water from it. Pretending to blow it clear, he put it to his lips and managed to produce three loud blasts. It was the usual signal to his men.

The big man stood there, smiling.

"I like a lad," he said, "who can take a ducking."

Robin was just as friendly as the stranger. "How are you known and what brings you here?" he asked.

"I'm known as John Little," replied the big man. "I seek Robin Hood."

Robin glanced up, suspicious. "Why, John Little?" he asked.

"To join him. I care not who knows."

Robin smiled at the defiant answer. "He's not far off," he promised.

Just then a band of men in Lincoln green came over the hill and down toward the bridge.

John Little clutched his staff tightly but made no attempt to flee.

"How now, good Master Robin?" asked Will Scarlet. "Is this fellow bothering you?"

John Little was astonished. "Be you really Robin Hood?" he asked.

Robin laughed. "I be."

For a moment, John Little looked even more astonished.

"Would you be of a mind to join us?" Will Scarlet asked. "You'll eat fresh meat every day, and have money in your poke."

John Little stuck out his huge hand. "I am your man," he said. Some of his new comrades winced as he shook hands with them.

Will Scarlet eyed the new member of the band from head to foot. He winked at the others. "What say you, lads? Shall we christen our infant?"

There was a short, sharp struggle before John Little was overcome by sheer numbers. They carried him, kicking and struggling, to the edge of the river and threw him into the water.

As he scrambled out, Will Scarlet tapped him gently on the shoulder.

"John Little," he said solemnly, "I dub thee Little John."

Robin stepped forward, his eyes merry. "Are you with us, Little John?"

"I am, indeed!"

"In faith, Will Scarlet," said Robin, "you christen like a true son of the Church." His face clouded. "Would we had some man in holy orders to care for our souls and tend our wounds."

"I know one," said Little John. "He is a holy hermit who lives near Alford Abbey. But he'd sooner break heads than mend them. His name is Friar Tuck."

THE FIGHT AT THE FORD

Friar Tuck, the hermit of Alford Abbey, was a plump fellow with a face like a healthy apple and more chins than were really neces-

sary. His hands were broad and muscular and he had good shoulders.

The present moment was a peaceful one. He was seated with his back against a giant oak and his face shone with contentment. All by himself, he was singing a duet: first in a high, shrill voice, then in a deep bass.

Robin arrived in time to hear the beginning of the song. After two more verses, he joined in, using a high voice and screeching out of tune.

As the final notes died away, the Friar realized that his duet was a real one. He charged around the tree to discover who was spoiling his song.

"Spy on me, will you," roared the Friar, "you meddling snoopy-nose!"

Robin made a gesture of peace. "Nay," he said, still laughing, "we should not quarrel who have sung together so sweetly."

Friar Tuck was not easily pacified. "What seek you here?" he roared.

Robin blinked. "Why," he said, in a mild voice to match his mild manner, "I come but to pray in yonder abbey. Is there no bridge?"

"None whatever," said Friar Tuck, more calmly, "but since you wish to pray, I'll not keep you from wading across as others do."

"Thank you," said Robin. "Would you lend me the breadth of your back to carry me over the stream?"

Too late Friar Tuck stared down at the sword that prodded his fat stomach.

"Since you press me with such arguments, I cannot refuse." And he walked down to the edge of the river, with Robin close behind. When he stepped into the water and bent his back, Robin sheathed his sword and climbed on the Friar's broad shoulders.

But Friar Tuck had a trick or two up the broad sleeves of his brown robe. As Robin slid to the ground, the Friar drew his own sword and pressed the point against Robin's chest.

"How now!" said Friar Tuck. "I carried you over. You can carry me back!"

Caught by surprise, Robin had no choice. He started off across the stream, staggering beneath his heavy load.

They had almost reached the shore, when Robin swung his hands up quickly, grasped the Friar by the back of the neck, and sent him crashing to the ground.

Before Friar Tuck could pull himself together, Robin forced him to enter the water again.

But Friar Tuck was not yet finished. As he waded through the water, his fingers were busy, unfastening the cord at the neck of his cloak. When Robin slid from his shoulders, he made sure that the cloak slid, too. It fell over Robin, covering his head and arms.

By the time Robin got himself clear, the Friar had picked up his sword and they were soon at it, sword to sword. They were eager to test each other's skill, as they had already tested their wits against each other. But they were interrupted by a band of horsemen.

It was the Sheriff and his men.

"Take him alive!" shouted De Lacy, delighted to have the outlaw delivered almost into his hands.

The horsemen spread out in a wide semicircle to cut off Robin's escape. But Friar Tuck came forward.

"You shall not interfere," he said, waving his sword in De Lacy's face, "until I have finished with him."

But De Lacy did not take the burly Friar seriously. "Throw him in the stream and stop his noise," he said, and several foresters started to obey.

Friar Tuck wasted no more time pleading with the Sheriff. "Come, lad," he called to Robin, "back to back."

In one bound Robin Hood was beside Friar Tuck, and they stood ready to defend each other, as the foresters swarmed around them.

De Lacy waited on his horse, watching for an opening. When he saw Friar Tuck move slightly away from Robin to strike at a forester, the Sheriff rode in close and knocked the priest to the ground with the flat of his sword.

With a second blow, he knocked Robin's sword from his hand. Unarmed, Robin dashed to a sheltering tree, where a forester came at him, sword in hand.

Without hesitating, Robin seized an overhanging branch and swung himself into the air. His feet crashed into the forester's face and knocked him down.

De Lacy whirled his horse around and charged at Robin, who was still swinging in the tree. At the right moment, he let himself go and knocked the Sheriff off the horse's back. Seizing the reins, he mounted the horse himself and turned the animal toward the river.

Bending low over the horse's mane, Robin reached for his hunting horn and blew a loud blast.

Now Robin had to hold off the angry Sheriff until his own band came to the rescue.

He tried to ride the horse across the stream and up the other side. But the bank was too wet and steep, so Robin set the horse loose. Nearby, Robin caught a glimpse of Lincoln green.

"Will Scarlet," he thought, "and Little John. Just in time."

Next Scathelock appeared, holding out a bow and quiver of arrows. Immediately, Robin was in the thick of the battle, and the foresters were ready to quit. Even De Lacy could not stop them.

Meanwhile, Friar Tuck was sitting up and rubbing his head. He could not remember what had hit him, but he had only to look around to see that he had missed a good fight. And there was the Sheriff, trying to catch his horse.

Suddenly the Friar's mind cleared. He sat up and whistled a shrill and peculiar whistle. From the direction of the abbey came a deep-throated baying.

Friar Tuck smiled and settled back, looking well satisfied with himself. He made no attempt to stop De Lacy, who was floundering through the stream, still trying to catch his frightened horse.

A few minutes later, the giant hound that Friar Tuck had summoned from the abbey bounded into the clearing and stopped at his master's feet. A brief command, and the hound leaped into the river after the Sheriff and pulled him to the shore.

De Lacy, who took such pleasure in making other men prisoners, was a prisoner himself.

A LORDLY GUEST

Back at Robin Hood's main camp, Stutely and two of the other outlaws tested the venison which they had been cooking over a wood fire. It was done at last, just in time, too, for they heard the others returning.

Stutely looked up with a smile which changed into a look of unbelief when he recognized Robin Hood's prisoner.

"You had good hunting, Master Robin."

"Aye," said Robin. "A lordly knight has consented to be our guest." Little John was leading a horse on which Sheriff De Lacy sat, blindfolded.

Robin Hood sat down at the rough table, loaded with roast game, huge flagons of ale, black bread, and cheese.

Scarlet and Little John helped the blindfolded prisoner to a seat at the foot of the table and whipped the bandage from his

eyes. De Lacy blinked and stared around the ring of faces.

Stutely growled and threw a portion of venison across the table. The Sheriff folded his arms defiantly.

"I have no taste for venison killed by poachers!" De Lacy protested.

Robin Hood shrugged and turned to Stutely, whose hand kept straying to the knife at his belt. "Can you put an edge on his appetite, Stutely?" Robin asked.

Stutely had been waiting for this. He leaned across the table and raised his wicked knife to De Lacy's throat. The threat was enough. De Lacy crammed the venison into his mouth.

Robin Hood called for a bowl of ale, and the outlaws rose to pledge the King. But before anyone could drink, Robin lowered his bowl and gazed steadily at De Lacy, who alone remained seated.

"My Lord Sheriff," Robin Hood said, "on your feet, sirrah!"

Reluctantly, De Lacy stood up.

"To Richard of England!" said Robin. The Sheriff made no move. "Speak up, man!" said Robin sharply.

Swallowing hard, De Lacy repeated the words.

"God grant him health and long life," said Robin.

Once again De Lacy repeated the words as though they made a bad taste in his mouth.

"Confusion to his enemies . . ." Robin went on.

"Confusion to his enemies . . ." came the echo.

The toast was drunk with noisy good fellowship.

"Now that you have pledged your king as a loyal subject," said Robin, "we'll speed you on your way."

"First," said Scarlet, "he must pay his debts."

The Friar began to scratch figures on the rough boards with his knife.

"Nine pennies for the meal," he began, while De Lacy watched anxiously. "And for that lad's wounded back, nine crowns."

"For my cracked head and the loss of my cattle," Scathelock shouted, "twenty shillings!"

"Twenty for my barn burned and my taxes

tripled!" shouted Adam. Then a babble broke out, as the outlaws listed their claims against De Lacy.

"Ten shillings for my dog maimed . . ."

"Five for the loss of my sow . . ."

"Four marks for my stolen horse . . ."

"Roughly," the Friar said, "one hundred shillings . . ." He raised his hand to scratch his head and his fingers touched the massive bump raised by the Sheriff's sword. He glared and added another fine to the list.

"*Two* hundred shillings."

De Lacy exploded in anger. "You thieving mock-priest! Why don't you join them, too?"

A look of surprise spread over the Friar's face. "God forgive me," he said. "It seems I have already done so!"

The outlaws roared with merriment at the Friar's words.

"Come," said Little John to the Sheriff, "let's see the color of your money."

Stutely separated the Sheriff's purse from his belt, and poured a stream of golden coins on the rough table.

"You'll pay for this," raged De Lacy.

"But first," said Robin Hood, "we'll make an example of you."

At his signal, the outlaws swarmed around De Lacy, tossing him roughly back and forth.

Then Stutely ran in with a pair of antlers which the men bound firmly around De Lacy's head. Still struggling, the Sheriff was hoisted on his horse and wedged firmly into the saddle, facing the horse's tail. His legs were tied together beneath the horse's body and his hands bound together as well.

As a final touch, Stutely put the horse's tail in the Sheriff's bound hands.

One of the outlaws smacked the horse on the rump and it leaped forward. And so the Sheriff returned to Nottingham, more furious than ever with Robin Hood and his band.

BAD NEWS FOR LADY MARIAN

Two years dragged by while King Richard was away in the Holy Land. Rumors drifted back to England that the Crusade was not going well.

Not long after, even worse news reached London. Richard was in prison! His powerful enemy, the Duke of Austria, had seized Richard and now held him under guard in a mountain fortress. The Duke would release Richard if his people could raise a huge ransom—a hundred and fifty thousand marks. It was a king's ransom, indeed.

In London, Queen Eleanor and Lady Marian waited anxiously for news. Would the Archbishop of Canterbury be able to raise such a huge ransom?

At last the Archbishop arrived, travel-stained and weary. "We are thirty thousand marks nearer our goal," said the Archbishop. "The monasteries have melted up their plate."

"God bless them," said the Queen. "What else?"

The Archbishop shook his head. "Madam," he said, "your own son, Prince John, has refused to contribute."

The Queen, reddening with shame, declared, "He shall not hold back. Tonight we leave for Nottingham."

The Queen's arrival in Nottingham was an unpleasant surprise for Prince John. It was no secret that he feared his mother, both for her courage and her honesty. As he stood in front of the great stone fireplace at Nottingham Castle, he tried to conceal his real feelings.

"Now that I know more money is needed for my brother's ransom," he said, "I'll order a public donation tomorrow in Nottingham Square."

John tried to sound sincere. "The truth is that my nobles and I are impoverished. I must support a huge army."

The Archbishop raised his eyebrows. "To protect whom against what?"

"To protect the kingdom, of course. For the past two years we have been cursed with an outlaw who loots the countryside."

"Who is this outlaw?"

"Robin Hood," said Prince John. "He that was named Robin Fitzooth before he took to Sherwood Forest to hide his misdeeds."

"It cannot be!" Marian sprang to Robin's defense. "Hugh Fitzooth is my father's chief forester. He and his son, Robin, are both men of honor."

"Hugh Fitzooth is dead," Prince John said brutally. "He was killed for shooting a king's

forester in the back. And his son has murdered threescore foresters since."

Marian stared at Prince John. "Whoever
killed Hugh Fitzooth murdered the King's
most loyal subject."

Marian turned to the Queen and knelt at
her feet. "Good Madam," she burst out, "Robin loves the King. I'm sure of it."

"He loves the King better in a foreign prison," sneered Prince John.

"Send me to Robin Fitzooth," Marian
begged. "I will prove to you his loyalty."

"I dare not, Marian." Queen Eleanor was
firm. "I have you in trust. I promised your
father."

"Please, Madam, if I could have an escort
. . ."

"No!" The Queen's reply was impatient.
"You shall not set foot outside the castle
walls."

Marian bowed her head. She could not
forget Prince John's sneering words. She was
sure they were lies, but how could she prove
it?

Later that day, she was still thinking
about this as she gazed from a window in
the upper corridor of the castle.

"Mistress Marian," said a voice. "Why so
sad?" It was Giles, a young page about fourteen years old. "Is there anything I can do,
my lady?"

Marian shook her head at Giles' question.
"The Queen has forbidden me to leave the
castle."

Giles sighed, "I wish Prince John would
forbid me," he said. "I've walked as far as
Jerusalem and back, making trips to Nottingham Town. I'm on my way there now to
fetch the Sheriff. Before I find him, I may
have to trudge halfway to Sherwood
Forest."

The page turned away down the corridor,
and Marian watched him go. If only she
might go in his place.

"Giles!" she called urgently. "Come back!"

THE MINSTREL AND
THE MILLER

Allan-a-Dale, the minstrel, looked over his
audience in the courtyard of the Silver Cross
Inn at Nottingham. Not much money there,
he guessed. There were a few loafers, a
beggar or two, a miller with a keen Welsh
face, and a page from the castle.

The minstrel winked at the miller and began to sing:

> "O, the Sheriff with threescore bowmen
> Rode out of Nottingham Town,
> But Robin Hood left those bowmen
> A-gasping on the ground."

At the end of the song, the minstrel wandered through the crowd, holding out his
lute for coins. But no one had a penny to
spare, except a young page from the castle.

"God bless you, young master," said the
minstrel, and he turned to leave.

The innkeeper shouted after him. "To
reach Clipstone, you must pass through Sherwood Forest. If you meet with the man you
sing about, you'll wish yourself back here."

The minstrel waved a careless good-bye
and continued on his way. The young page
hurried after him.

"May I keep you company?" the page
asked.

"Aye, lad, and welcome."

Back in the courtyard of the Inn, the miller with the dark Welsh face was thoughtful.
Suddenly, he picked up his bag of flour and
hurried off after the minstrel and the page.

Soon, Allan-a-Dale and the page left the
broad highway and took a narrow footpath
that plunged into Sherwood Forest. Behind
them came Midge the Miller, his bag of
flour on his shoulder, his staff in his hand.

The farther the three travelers went into
the forest, the darker and gloomier it became. The miller kept glancing anxiously
from side to side. He was glad to have

company and kept the other travelers in sight. He was not far behind when he heard a shrill sound.

"Would that be a bird now?" he asked.

"Aye," said the minstrel. "What did you think it was?"

"No matter now." The miller stared around at the dark forest. "I'd have ye sing me a song." He took a penny from his purse and looked at it as if he hated to let it go.

"What'll you have?" asked Allan.

"The song about Robin Hood. Here is my penny," said the miller.

The minstrel took the penny and began to sing:

"O, the Sheriff with threescore bowmen—"

The song broke off suddenly as three figures appeared and blocked the path. Robin Hood was in the center, with Little John on one side and Will Scarlet on the other.

"Sing on, fellow!" said Robin Hood.

The minstrel had been wishing for a larger audience. Perhaps these fellows would pay to hear about their own deeds.

So the minstrel continued:

" 'Now sit you down, proud Sheriff,
And taste our woodland cheer.'
'I will not sit,' the Sheriff said,
'Nor eat of stolen deer.' "

He glanced up expectantly at the end. "I trust you liked the song, masters."

"Is that all?" growled Little John.

"Well . . . er . . . no," said the minstrel. Allan-a-Dale cleared his throat and began to make up another verse as he went along.

"Now, here's to good kind Robin Hood
And his bold yeomanry;
There's no better men than Scarlet
Or Little John in all our fair countree . . ."

The last line ended in a gabble that was too much for the outlaws. They threw back their heads and roared with laughter. When Allan-a-Dale realized that they had been teasing him all along, he laughed too and held out his lute to the outlaws, hoping for a penny or two.

Robin Hood pushed it aside. "Nay," he said. "There's only one man who can pass the hat in Sherwood Forest." He reached out and caught hold of the miller who was trying to sneak past.

"I've spent my last penny," mumbled the miller. "And there's naught in the bag save flour."

"Why, then," said Robin, "we'll empty it out. If there's no gold, we'll pay you for the flour. If there is gold you'll make a contribution to the poor."

The young page interrupted. "Would you rob a poor miller?"

Little John brushed the page aside as the miller suddenly changed his plea.

"Spare me my flour," said Midge, "and you shall have the money." He put down his stick, rolled up his sleeves, and started to

root around in the bag, as if searching for hidden coins.

While they were still leaning over, watching, Midge pulled his hands out of the sack and threw two large handfuls of flour in their faces. As the outlaws staggered back, Midge picked up his cudgel and beat them over the shoulders.

"I'll dust your coats," he shouted. In the scuffle, Robin managed to pull the empty sack over the miller's head. When Little John bellowed with laughter, the page rushed in and started beating Robin with the miller's staff. Robin received several hearty whacks before Little John lifted the page right off the ground and held him struggling.

"Let me go, you monster!" cried the page. "Let me go, I say!"

Robin looked up quickly at the sound of that voice. "Hey, John!" shouted Robin. "Give me that lad!"

Without effort, the big man heaved the page through the air into Robin's outstretched arms. The page's hat tumbled off and a mass of long, dark hair fell down about the page's face. Robin recognized Lady Marian.

"Let me down, you thief!" Marian raged.

"Well, well," said Robin and glanced uncomfortably at the miller.

"Persuade Midge to join us if you can," said Robin Hood to Little John.

He whirled around, with Lady Marian over his shoulder, and set off through the forest. Little John picked up the miller and followed after.

Allan-a-Dale watched them go, with sad eyes like an abandoned dog.

Scarlet turned back. "Come along, minstrel. The more the merrier!"

A KING'S RANSOM

Dusk had fallen in Sherwood Forest. The campfire flickered on the faces of Robin Hood's men, as they rested after the day's hunting. In the shadows, Friar Tuck and Lady Marian kept up a continual murmur of talk.

At last the slender girl and the burly Friar joined the group around the campfire.

Robin Hood smiled. His tone was light, but his question was serious. "Has the good friar persuaded you to join us?"

Marian took the question seriously. "No. But he has convinced me of your honesty. Yet one other thing I would know. Could you choose otherwise, would you still be outlaws?"

For a moment, Robin gazed into the fire, as if the answer to the girl's question was to be found there.

"The greenwood has its beauty and we find freedom here . . ." He paused. "But we are banished men, my lady."

Marian seemed to consider Robin's words, as if testing their truth. At last, she put her hand on Robin's arm.

"I will clear your name," she promised, "if you will give me every penny you possess."

Robin hesitated. "What would you do with the money?"

"I'd give it towards the King's ransom

tomorrow at Nottingham. Then everyone would see how much more loyal you are than Prince John. The Prince says he is too poor to contribute."

Little John growled. "Prince John and the Sheriff have stolen enough gold to ransom the King twice over."

"The Prince denies that," said Marian. "He swears you outlaws dread the King's return."

"There is only one answer to such a monstrous lie," said Robin.

Robin emptied the contents of his purse into the Friar's lap, and soon the money poured in. One after another, each member of the band took part.

Proudly Robin handed the huge collection of coins to Marian.

"Friar Tuck and I will see you safely sheltered in Alford Abbey tonight," said Robin. "On the morrow, 'twill be safer if he alone escorts you to Nottingham."

Nottingham Square was crowded when Friar Tuck and Lady Marian arrived there the following morning. The Friar took one look at the crowd and handed the heavy purse to the girl, who began pushing her way toward the church steps.

Queen Eleanor was sitting there beside Prince John and the Archbishop of Canterbury. In front of them was a large oak table for gifts to meet the King's ransom.

Marian reached the steps and knelt down in front of the old Queen.

"My Lady," said Marian, "I humbly beg your forgiveness. Love of England compelled me to seek out the King's friends and prove to you their loyalty."

Approaching the counting table, Marian flung down the bag with the money from Sherwood Forest.

"This purse," Marian announced loudly, "was given freely by Robin Fitzooth and his outlawed band. With it they sent their prayers for King Richard and his swift return."

De Lacy turned, protesting, to the Queen. "Should such tainted coin be mingled with the gifts of honorable men? Were the sum a thousand marks, our noble King himself would scorn to buy his freedom with blood money."

A voice, suspiciously like the voice of Robin Hood, sang out from the crowd.

"Well said, Sheriff," it called. "Where's *your* thousand marks?"

Robin's remark was taken up and repeated again and again. "A thousand marks from the Sheriff! Where is your thousand marks?"

The Archbishop rose and lifted his hands for quiet. "My good people, your outburst is premature. I am confident the Sheriff is but waiting his turn."

Prince John flashed a look at De Lacy. "What say you, Sir Sheriff?"

De Lacy managed a smile. "My Lords, you'll find my loyalty will meet the test." He shouted toward the house. "Bring forth my coffer!" Two servants in the Sheriff's livery came forward with a small silver coffer and delivered it to De Lacy, who placed it on the table.

Meanwhile, things were happening in the Sheriff's house. The servants were suddenly seized and bound by some of Robin Hood's band who promptly searched the house for more gold and found it. They filled a large wooden chest, and dragged it near the door.

Outside, the contents of the Sheriff's coffer had been counted. The total was eleven hundred and eighty-seven marks.

"There you are," De Lacy said smugly. "You asked for a thousand, I have given nearly twelve hundred." He bowed to the Queen. "The gift has left me penniless, but I would to Heaven I could give ten thousand more."

As De Lacy spoke this insincere wish, a palmer pushed his way to the steps. It was Robin Hood in disguise.

"Heaven has heard you, my Lord High Sheriff," and he pointed to the large chest which two of his men, dressed in the Sheriff's livery, were dragging down the steps. They dumped it on the counting table so that coins spilled out in a golden flood.

Before De Lacy could protest, the Archbishop had risen. "Now God be thanked," he said. "The deliverance of our King is assured!"

As the Queen walked to her horsedrawn litter, the crowd started cheering the Sheriff of Nottingham. The cheers were led by several men at the front of the crowd. Two brawny fellows grabbed De Lacy and lifted him to their shoulders. They started a regular parade.

De Lacy looked down anxiously at his bearers. He was amazed to find himself staring into the amused eyes of Robin Hood. "You—you . . ." He nearly choked with rage. "Set me down! Down, I say!"

Robin Hood laughed and winked at Little John. "He said 'down.' "

"So be it," said the big man.

As easily as a child throws a ball, they swung the Sheriff clear of their shoulders and heaved him into the center of the castle moat.

AMBUSH IN SHERWOOD FOREST

From a tower window in Nottingham Castle, two men stared down into the moonlit courtyard. They saw the Archbishop directing the loading of the chests filled with ransom money into huge wagons.

"Tomorrow," said Prince John slowly, "that money will be on its way to save the King it should have helped to over-throw."

John's face was very thoughtful. He stroked his beard and glanced sideways at De Lacy.

"I have in mind a desperate plan," he said to De Lacy in his quiet, most dangerous voice. "Have you those among your bowmen you would trust? They must be men who hate Robin Hood and fear the King's return as we do."

"I have many such men, sire." De Lacy's eyes gleamed. "What would you have them do?"

"Disguise themselves as Robin Hood's men and steal our money back!"

De Lacy frowned. "How, my Lord?"

"It could be done tomorrow when the Queen and the Archbishop are traveling through Sherwood Forest with the ransom money."

" 'Tis a bold plan," admitted the Sheriff, "and it could succeed except for that girl."

"Maid Marian?"

"She alone has met the real outlaws face to face."

"Then the girl must not travel with the Queen," the Prince decided. He looked down the corridor toward a doorway where

Hubert, his personal bodyguard, was waiting.

"Hubert," he ordered, "bring the Lady Marian here. But let her believe that his Grace the Archbishop desires her presence."

Prince John caught De Lacy by the arm. "As for you, Sir Sheriff, send forth your men at dawn, dressed in their usual livery. Bid them ride a full twenty miles down the Great Road through Sherwood Forest before they change to Lincoln green. Then they may lie in wait for the convoy."

De Lacy had hardly gone before Prince John heard Hubert returning with the girl. When she saw only Prince John, she drew back. "My Lord Archbishop? Is he here?"

"This way, my Lady," and Prince John led the way to a door which opened into a tower room. The girl walked in before she realized that it was a trap.

Marian stared after him, horrified, as he closed the door and locked her in.

And Prince John retired to bed, well satisfied. Long before he awoke the next morning, a picked company of the Sheriff's bowmen were on their way to Sherwood Forest.

It was dawn when the leader of this band halted his men beneath a giant beech tree in the forest. They dismounted and quickly changed their livery for Lincoln green.

But someone was watching, for Robin Hood's men always knew who came and went through the depths of Sherwood Forest.

The guard this time was Stutely, and he had already spotted the slow-moving convoy carrying the ransom money to London. When he realized that the Sheriff's men were planning to ambush the convoy, he slipped away to a clearing. Here he sent up a whistling arrow to warn Robin Hood of trouble in the forest.

The Archbishop was riding at the head of the convoy, his eyes alert for danger, when armed men sprang suddenly at him from all sides.

His guards were dragged from their saddles, and the leader of the ambush stood in front of the Archbishop, a short sword in his hand and two bowmen at his side.

"In the name of the King and of the Holy Church," said the Archbishop sternly, "stand aside and let us pass."

"We own no king save Robin Hood," said the leader. "Search the wagons!"

Two of the disguised foresters grabbed the money chest while others held off the escort guards. They had nearly swung the largest chest clear when Queen Eleanor stepped out of her litter.

"Hold!" The Queen's voice was firm and unafraid. "Put down that chest."

The men hesitated, but the leader had his orders. "Bring out those chests, I say. Pay no heed to the old bellwether."

The Archbishop's face tightened at these words. As he drew his sword to attack the leader of the ambush, Robin Hood and his men galloped out of the woods, and the attackers became the attacked.

Arrows flew and swords flashed as the men battled back and forth. But Robin Hood's men made the most of their advantage.

At last Robin stood before the Queen. "I pray you're unharmed, my Lady."

Queen Eleanor eyed him with scorn. "No thanks to your cut-throat knaves!"

"Those thieves were no men of mine," pleaded Robin. He whirled around and called for Little John. The outlaw came forward, holding a captive forester.

"Whom do you serve?" the big man growled.

"The Sheriff of Nottingham." The prisoner showed the livery which he had discarded for Lincoln green.

With an effort, the Queen controlled her anger and turned to Robin Hood.

"Robin Fitzooth, the King shall hear of you and your stout lads. I shall even forgive you for stealing my Lady Marian again."

"Marian?" Robin was puzzled. "My Lady, I have not seen her since she returned. Is she not with you?"

"She slipped away last night," said the Queen.

"At least, that is what Prince John told you," said the Archbishop.

"We shall return at once," the Queen said. "The girl may be in danger."

"Nay, my lady," said Robin. "Let me go."

JUSTICE FOR THE SHERIFF

It was dusk when a band of men in the Sheriff's livery rode over the drawbridge and into Nottingham Castle. Prince John and De Lacy were happy to see that the saddlebags of the returning foresters were full and bulging.

The drawbridge was raised as the last man trotted through. Prince John waited impatiently as four men came nearer, their heads bent beneath the saddle bags. Suddenly, Robin Hood's knife was pressed against Prince John's stomach, while the three others held De Lacy.

"Lead us to the Maid Marian, or you forfeit your lives." Robin Hood emphasized the threat with a prod of his knife. Cursing, Prince John led them to the room in which Marian was a prisoner.

Robin pulled Marian quickly out of the cell, as Little John pushed the Prince inside and locked the door.

The outlaws still had De Lacy in their midst as they made their way back to the courtyard. Keeping one eye on the guards who paced the outer walls, the outlaws moved quietly toward the stables where the band was waiting.

"Would you have us rush the warders, and bring the drawbridge down?" Little John asked.

Robin Hood shook his head. "Nay, we

came as Sheriff's men and we'll leave as such. Escort to a Queen's lady. When you see the drawbridge lowered, ride out in good order."

Marian and the outlaws mounted while Robin walked toward the drawbridge, leading his horse, and prodding the Sheriff with a knife in his ribs.

"Give the order to lower the drawbridge," Robin prompted the Sheriff.

"Lower the drawbridge!" De Lacy shouted. In response, one of the warders heaved on the heavy chain that controlled the drawbridge. As soon as it lowered, the band, with Marian in the center, rode calmly out in the moonlight.

When the group had passed, Robin Hood swung his horse around so that he blocked the way between the Sheriff and the warders.

"Now sir," he said, raising his knife, "here's payment long overdue."

There were beads of sweat on De Lacy's forehead and his eyes were wide with terror. "Spare me!" he begged. "I swear upon my honor as a knight that I will not cry out, if you but spare me!"

"So be it," said Robin, and swung himself into the saddle. But he had not gone far before De Lacy screamed, "Halt that man!"

The warders sprang forward and thrust out their spears, blocking the drawbridge. Robin drew his sword and cut the first man down, but a second man drove his spear upward into Robin's shoulder, causing him to fall sideways off his horse.

On his feet again, his wounded arm dangling, Robin slashed his way past another warder. From the corner of his eye, he saw De Lacy turn the wheel that raised the bridge. He must cross before it was too late. As he rushed out, De Lacy followed and grasped his legs as the drawbridge slowly lifted upward.

Inch by inch, the drawbridge moved up with the two men struggling desperately together. Soon it would close and they would be crushed. But Robin gave one kick and freed himself. He threw his leg over the top of the bridge in time to save himself and jumped into the moat. De Lacy, screaming horribly, was killed as the drawbridge slammed against the wall.

In the water, Robin was a target for the castle guards. But the outlaws had turned back to rescue their leader. While others took care of the guards, Little John pulled Robin to the bank, and the band carried him to their hiding place.

ROBIN HOOD AND THE KING

Allan-a-Dale, the merry minstrel, was asleep, snoring gently, at the foot of the Lookout Tree. Little John nudged him with his foot.

"Hey, there, minstrel," the giant roared. "Wake up and sing!"

Allan-a-Dale opened one eye.

"I'll sing a new song," he offered, and began to hum, trying to find the right tune and the right words for a new ballad about Robin Hood.

As he was composing his song, Marian came out of the cave, which had become her home.

Marian poured out a bowl of barley broth from a kettle over the fire, and took it to another cave, where Robin made his headquarters. He was dressed in Lincoln green and in no mood for sick man's soup.

"Drink this," she coaxed. He refused.

The sound of a screaming signal arrow brought Robin to his feet. He pushed Marian aside. "Stay here," he ordered, picked up his short sword, and rushed out into the clearing.

Very soon a stranger appeared. He was a knight, all alone, clad from head to foot in black armor. His visor was closed, and he wore no coat-of-arms or other markings.

"Which of you is Robin Hood?"

"I am," said Robin. "What seek you here?"

"I come to rid this forest of outlaws."

There was a growl from the circle of men who closed in around the stranger.

"Come you from Prince John?" Robin asked.

"I come in the King's name."

Robin's face was bitter. " 'Tis ever in the King's name. And the true King not here to tell right from wrong." His tone became curt. "Take off your helm."

The knight straightened up on his horse. "Do not think to order me." His voice had an edge of steel.

"Take off your helm," shouted Friar Tuck, "or I'll knock it about your ears."

Slowly the strange knight doffed his helmet and looked around the circle. The outlaws gasped as they recognized the piercing blue eyes and red-gold hair of King Richard!

Awkwardly, they dropped to their knees. Would he ever believe how loyal they were in their hearts?

Robin spoke for them all. "Pardon our rash and careless words, my Lord!"

The King dismounted and walked over to where Robin knelt. "I'll forgive you more than that. England stands deep in debt to you and your brave bowmen."

He drew his sword and tapped the outlaw on the shoulder. "Robin Fitzooth, henceforth you will be known as Robin, Earl of Locksley."

Robin stood up. All around him, his men were dancing, cheering, and clapping him on the back. The noise brought Marian from the cave and she stared at the cheerful scene, with the King in the center.

She heard the King say, "I had hoped to find the Lady Marian among you."

Marian came forward and the men made way for her. "My liege," she said, "have you news of my father?"

Richard motioned her to rise. "He awaits you at Huntingdon, where the Queen has vowed you are to marry the Earl of Locksley."

Marian could hardly control her dismay. "My Lord King, have I no choice?"

"None," said King Richard sternly.

The girl turned to Robin. "Robin Fitzooth, have you naught to say?"

"Who am I," replied Robin, "to question the wishes of my Sovereign King and the Queen Mother?"

"Well said, my Earl of Locksley," said the King, and Marian spun around. The men were all grinning, and Friar Tuck motioned for Robin to kiss the girl.

When Robin saw that Richard was nodding his approval, Robin kissed the Lady Marian, and whirled her around in a dance of joy.

Allan-a-Dale ran his fingers across the strings of his lute and sang softly:

"Oh, I'll sing a song, a rollicky song,
As I roll along my way,
With a hey derry die and a derry die do."

The merry minstrel, Allan-a-Dale, was very well satisfied. His head was filled with tunes and stories about the outlaw who became an earl and married a lady. Who can tell? He might write a ballad that would last a thousand years.

GOLIATH II

ONCE upon a time in a far-away jungle, there lived a tiny elephant. His name was Goliath the Second, and he was just barely five inches tall. He was so small he couldn't even pull up a daisy.

"I'll never grow up," said little Goliath sadly. "I'll never be a giant elephant like my father."

His father, great Goliath the First, was the biggest tusker in the whole jungle, and leader of the elephant herd. He was so huge and powerful he could uproot the biggest tree without even trying.

"It's not fair," he grumbled. "Why should I have a little bit of a son who can't even pull up a daisy?"

But Goliath's mother, like most mothers, was proud of her little son no matter what. She didn't care one whit about uprooting trees or pulling up daisies.

"Don't worry, Goliath," she said, "brute strength isn't everything. You'll amount to something one day, just wait and see."

Raising such a tiny son in the dense and savage jungle was a big problem.

Mother Goliath's number one problem was Raja, a crafty old tiger who could hardly take his greedy eyes off little Goliath.

"I've always been curious to taste an elephant," said old Raja, "and now at last I've found one just bite size."

But Goliath's mother wasn't taking any chances. She kept a sharp eye on her little son every minute of the day. And at night she tucked him safely into bed in an empty bird's nest high on a tree limb.

Each day the elephants took a dip in the river. And little Goliath was left on the bank to splash and play in one of his mother's huge footprints.

"Stay right here where I can see you," she warned. "Don't you dare leave your pond."

Goliath was getting tired of being treated like a baby.

"I'm nearly eight years old," he said. "I'm old enough to look out for myself."

One day when his mother wasn't looking, Goliath left his footprint pond and wandered off down the elephant trail.

It was a perfect day for running away. The jungle was sunny and warm and very, very quiet. There was only the gentle whisper of the breeze and the sound of footsteps —soft, velvety footsteps. And they weren't Goliath's.

Suddenly he saw two pale yellow eyes peering through the grass. It was old Raja!

Goliath tried to run but he tripped on his trunk and fell flat on his face. Raja sprang into the air. But he never came down!

Something had old Raja by the tail. It was Goliath's mother—and she was furious!

"You bloodthirsty old scoundrel!" she screamed. She swung him round and round like a yoyo until his head was spinning.

Then with all her strength, Goliath's mother sent that old tiger flying high over the treetops, and all the way across the river to the far end of the jungle.

That was the end of old Raja. At least the old tiger was never seen again in that part of the jungle.

But that wasn't the end of little Goliath's troubles. For one thing, his mother gave him a good sound spanking with a blade of grass.

This didn't hurt Goliath half as much as one scornful look from his father, great Goliath the First.

Goliath had broken one of the first laws of the herd. A runaway elephant is called a

rogue and a traitor and treated as a criminal. Little Goliath had never felt quite so small in all his life. As an elephant, he was a failure.

One afternoon, as big Goliath led the herd down. the elephant trail toward the river, something happened. A most terrifying thing. There in the path was a fuzzy little creature with black beady eyes and a string tail.

"Mouse!" cried big Goliath. "It's a mouse! Run—run for your lives!"

The herd went crashing off through the jungle in a wild stampede, and leaped into the river.

There they stayed, trembling with terror, and with only the tips of their trunks sticking out of the water.

Only little Goliath stood his ground. He didn't move a muscle or blink an eye.

"What's the trouble, Buster?" said the mouse. "Are you scared stiff?"

"I'm not scared at all," said Goliath. "I'm just as big as you are."

"That's not the point. I'm a mouse and you're an elephant. And elephants are afraid of mice."

"Why?" asked Goliath.

"I'll show you why!" said the mouse. In a flash he seized Goliath by the trunk, whirled him into the air and slammed him to the ground. Then the mouse jumped up and down on Goliath's head and pinned him to the ground by his ears.

"Do you give up, Jumbo?"

"Never," said Goliath.

And with a wild kick he sent them both tumbling in the grass.

They rolled over and over and came closer to the edge of a steep cliff. Down below an old crocodile was waiting for someone to drop in for dinner—just anyone.

The mouse pushed Goliath toward the edge.

"Over you go, Buster!" he said.

But Goliath saw the crocodile. Desperately, he grabbed for the mouse's tail, and seized it in his trunk. Then with a sudden jerk he swung the mouse out over the cliff, right over the wide open jaws of the crocodile.

"Please don't let me down," cried the mouse. "I give up! You win, ole pal, ole pal! Okay?"

"Okay," said Goliath, and the battle was over.

As a reward for his great victory, Goliath was given the very highest position in the elephant herd—a place of honor on his proud father's head.

And the whole herd kept a kindly eye on little Goliath—for they didn't want to lose him.

Happiest of all was Goliath's mother. "I always knew you'd amount to something one day," she said proudly.

PORTUGAL
Beside the Sea

FROM the road curving down through the hills above, the fishing village of Nazaré seems deserted in the bright sunlight, a cluster of white, cubed-shaped houses, with cobblestone streets cutting down the steep slope to the sea. As we approach, we see that the town is not actually all white; the house fronts gleam with the high glaze of colored tiles—some with small floral patterns, others with geometric designs. Nor is the town empty, but everyone is down on the beach, for the sardine fishing fleet is in.

THE FLEET IS IN

On the beach, too, the scene is full of pattern and color, starting with the men themselves. For the men of Nazaré love plaids. They wear plaids patched with other plaids, all faded from sun and salt air and water to soft tones, but still strong and lively of line. Barefooted, the men stride briskly across the sands or stand in clusters along the beachfront street, discussing affairs of the day; on their heads, above the geometric tangle of the plaids, they wear black stocking caps.

No less colorful are their boats, pulled far up on the beach in a jumbled maze of broad curves and pointed, upswung prows. For their small size the boats are markedly sturdy in build, but gaudy and fanciful in decoration, often featuring lucky wide-open eyes on their prows to help in guiding them over the pathless seas. Sturdiness is more important than grace in the fishing boats of Nazaré, for the surf which rolls in here on the beach comes straight from the wild, cold Atlantic. And the offshore swells are far from gentle. Though the sea may stretch calm and glittering today, under the hot sun, by tomorrow it may be smashing rough. This is why the boats are pulled high on the beach, hauled there for safekeeping by teams of oxen who now lie placidly about on the sand.

These boats, like the fishing folk themselves, are said to date back to the ancient days when seagoing tradesmen of Phoenicia, off at the eastern end of the Mediterranean Sea, set out from the ports of Tyre and

Street musicians in a seaside town use some strange old instruments.

These Portuguese fishermen discuss the sardine catch beside their high-prowed boats.

The beach of Nazaré is a lively gathering place for the people of the town.

The women and girls often bring their sewing and knitting down to the beach.

Sidon, sailed the length of the deep-blue inland sea, and then dared to pass between the towering rocks of the Gates of Hercules (we know one side of the "gate" as Gibraltar today) into the fearful ocean beyond. So the Phoenicians, more than a thousand years before Christ, were the first of the ancient sailors to brave the legendary dangers of the Outer Sea with its rumored sea serpents and hungry monsters and, off in the storm-tossed mists, the yawning Edge of the Earth. The Phoenicians dared and, hugging the coast, sailed far to the north—some say as far as Britain, bargaining there for tin. Some say they found good trade along the way and sent out settlers to found new market towns along the coast of what is now Portugal. As we gaze into the stern, dark faces of the seafaring villagers, it is easy to see hints of the East, of Asia, in their strong profiles and flashing eyes.

WOMEN AT WORK

The women, busy at a dozen tasks—sorting fish, spreading some of the sardines out in shiny, salty ranks to dry, mending nets, piling high their baskets with silvery harvest—these women are more somberly dressed than their checker-trousered men. But all over Portugal, the village women manage a flourish of bright aprons and bright scarves over drab dresses, and wear hoops of gold in their ears. Everywhere they walk with the grace born of balancing burdens on the head, be the burden a basket of fish, a tall clay water jug with an ancestry as old as that of the boats, a bundle of laundry, or a wide, shallow basket of vegetables topped with a bunch of fire-bright flowers.

Fiercest and most independent of Portuguese women are the "varinas," the witty, vivacious fishwives. When they reach the market place with their baskets, the real fun begins, for the Portuguese love to bargain, and the great art is in knowing how much to overprice at the start and when, after lively banter, to relent and clinch the deal.

The market, of course, offers more than fish. Other country women have risen at dawn or before to bring in their vegetables. Over the winding, hilly lanes they walked barefoot, with heavily laden broad baskets on their heads, clutching their shawls more snugly against the early morning chill. Out at the highway they waited for the rattle and chug of the city-bound bus to sound around the curve. Before the bus reaches town each day, the roof is packed with baskets; the seats, with chattering women. At the stop in town, the baskets are handed down, and the women, hoisting them briskly to their heads, start at a jog trot for the market square, for first come often means first sold.

HARVEST OF THE SEA

Back at the beach, the greater part of the fleet's catch is sold at auction for canning and export. The Portuguese, who have a genius for doing things a little differently from other people, have their own individual auction technique. Instead of calling for bids, starting low and having bidders top each other until a batch goes to the highest bidder, the Portuguese auctioneer starts with a hundred and counts backward with astonishing speed. Thus the first bid is always the highest; the trick, for the buyer, lies in outguessing his competitors, getting his bid in ahead of theirs, yet not extravagantly early.

The sardines, which are canned in excellent native olive oil, have won a worldwide market for themselves. Indeed, fishing is the country's second most important industry, with tuna, cod and shellfish helping to keep the fleets plying the year round.

Launching the sardine boats is a task for teams of oxen or for many strong backs.

The women of the town are kept busy sorting the sardine catch as the men bring it ashore.

The women of Portugal find it preferable to carry their burdens on their heads.

"Moliceiros" are the slender, low-slung boats of the seaweed gatherers.

Far to the north the huge fishing boats, which lie tilted on the sands of the deep bathing beaches, are differently fashioned, with high, jutting prows and sterns sweeping about in a full half-circle curve. And back from the northern coast lie the lagoons where the seaweed gatherers ply their trade, for fish is not the only valuable harvest yielded by the sea. Salt is collected on the open flats, and seaweed, high in mineral content, is gathered on boats called "moliceiros." These are slender, far too delicate in line for the rigors of the open sea; they sweep up elegantly to a swan-necked prow, with midships dipping to the water line for ease in raking aboard the water-heavy weeds. The boatmen, wearing short white tunics and helmets, pole their way about the weed beds, raking up the seaweed into piles so high that from the shore it seems that the boats must surely be sinking under the load. Sometimes the men wade out into the icy waters, with their long-handled rakes; but

the fortunate ones have these quaint and lovely boats, each the work of a master craftsman whose skill is the product of many generations. These men, it is said, work without formal plans, their keen, trained eyes visualizing the form of the slender boat complete in the as yet uncut tree.

Of course not all the Portuguese fishing fleets have the charm of a long and colorful

The boatmen pole their way about the shallow, seaweed-laden flats in their high-sailed boats.

heritage. Many boats are equipped with motors and radio; instead of setting their nets and waiting for the fish to fill them, these can move swiftly to spots where schools of sardine or tuna have been sighted. But the time-hallowed traditions of Portugal's men of the sea center around the colorful, highly individualistic craft and their sturdy seamen, still often clad in the bright, black and yellow woolen shirts and black stocking caps which have been the garb of their fathers for long generations back. Before setting sail, they still gather bareheaded on the beaches to receive the blessing of the local priest and the prayers of the villagers for a good catch and a safe return from the sea.

THE WINE OF OPORTO

Down the rocky reaches of the Douro River ply the "ribeiros" or "rebelos," spoon-shaped vessels whose design goes back also to the Phoenician times. They wallow along among the shoals and sandbars with a huge square sail bellying full blown. With flat bottoms designed to withstand the grinding river bottom, decks loaded with lashed-on casks of precious wine, these are the last of the highly individual boat designs of Portugal we encounter, and our first glimpse of another most important and colorful industry rooted deep in the country's dreaming past. This is winemaking, and the country's famous wine, of course, is port.

In the upper valley of the Douro the vineyards are tucked into narrow, man-made terraces high on the mountain slopes. In the winter, harsh mountain winds and rainstorms attack the terraces, washing out chunks of wall and precious topsoil. Constant rebuilding and repairs are needed to keep the terraces in shape. In the spring, the vines must be pruned. During the summer there are insects to fight, and the sun to be kept from

Grapes for Portugal's wine industry are grown on terraces of the upper Douro valley.

The men of the Douro valley dance at the festival celebrating the grape harvest.

Out into the vineyards go the women with baskets almost as high as a man. Down the rows they move, their bright-colored head kerchiefs looking from a distance like huge rainbow-hued butterflies bobbing among the vines. As their nimble fingers strip the vines and heap the baskets high with purple clusters, the men carry the filled baskets off down the steep, winding paths. Single file, the long lines of men stride along while the leader pipes a tune.

Into huge stone tanks go the clusters of grapes, and when they are all collected comes the crushing, a bone-tiring task turned, with typical Portuguese flair, into a festival. First the men roll up their trousers and scrub legs and feet. Then they lower themselves into the grape-filled tank. Linking arms, they walk slowly, in high-stepping rhythm, across the mass of fruit, crushing it underfoot. Behind them a piper begins to play; the tune is taken up by another and a drum pounds out the beat. The wine crushers keep time, even as the music quickens. The faster the music, the harder and faster

burning the plants. Finally, in late September or October, the fat clusters of grapes turn purple-blue, and harvesttime is at hand.

Now, by comparison, the whole rest of the year seems like one long, drowsy siesta. For now everything must be done at once, and all at top speed. The grapes must be picked at the moment of full ripeness, their juice sluiced into the waiting vats at the peak of their rich flavor.

These girls are picking the grapes that will be used to make Portugal's famous port wine.

they stomp. Now their voices join the music in a wild, free song; fatigue is forgotten as the sweet juice bubbles over the crushed pulp, and they dance in a sea of purple up to their thighs.

The juice, slowly fermenting into wine, remains in the vats until spring. Then a native brandy is added to stop the fermentation, and the ruby liquid is transferred to oaken casks, each carefully marked with the year of vintage. Nowadays some casks are shipped by rail or truck to Oporto; but many still travel the ancient river highway, lashed to the decks of flat-bottomed rebelos for the sixty-mile journey down the Douro.

As the casks are unloaded from creaking oxcarts and made secure on deck, up go the square sails, if the day is brisk. If there is no wind, oars may be fitted into locks; or the boatmen walk the decks, shoving at long poles rammed into the rocky bottom. Sometimes the boats are towed along by a line of men bent double against the pull of the rope as they walk a towpath on the shore. But powered by wind or the strong arms of men, through rushing currents or calm waters, the skilled rebelo navigator brings his precious cargo through the treacherous waters and safely down the gorge.

Along the shores, when the men have time to look, a quiet pastoral scene drifts by. There are huge old windmills whose wing-like, cloth-clad arms provide in many places the only source of power. They stand like peaceful beacons of the past against the blue sky. Mules or burros, laden with grain, trot by at their leisurely pace. Women, carrying on their heads the earthen water jars called "canecas," watch with quiet eyes the passage of the square-sailed boat.

As the boat nears Oporto, life along the riverbanks quickens its pace. Tile-roofed, bright-colored houses appear, tucked into the cliffs along one bank. On the stone steps of the bridges, women gather as of old, washing their clothes, and gossiping.

On the far side of the gorge, where the hills are mostly barren, is Villa Nova da Gaia, journey's end for our rebelos. Here the wine casks are unloaded and stored in enormous caves until their contents are sufficiently aged for export. Most will be shipped to England, where port is a great favorite. Since 1703 England and Portugal have enjoyed a treaty which assures Britain a steady supply of port by keeping import taxes low.

IN FORESTS OF CORK

As little touched by modern ways is Portugal's cork industry. The cork forests in her highlands supply half the world's cork. These trees belong to one of the few varieties in the world which can survive without their bark. If it is stripped off with care, it will grow thick enough in nine or ten years to be stripped again; and since the bark alone is used, the cycle can continue profitably during the entire 120- to 150-year life span of the tree.

The bark is removed in two long strips, each ax blow being exactly calculated not to graze the tender skin beneath. The thick corky bark is stacked in piles, and the gleaming bare trunks, now pale yellow-gray, are left exposed to the wind and weather, and soon turn warm red-brown. As the bark grows back, they darken again, until after a number of years the spongy coat once more is thick enough for use.

While some of the men strip the trees, others sort the bark piled high and load it in heaps on oxcarts. These two-wheeled carts, their solid, spokeless wheels dating back to the days when Roman legions crossed the land with their supplies on just such carts, are found everywhere outside the cities in Portugal. Down the quiet, dusty roads they creak, unoiled wheels rasping their soft complaint. The oxen themselves are harnessed from the shoulder with ornamented yokes called "cangas," often hundreds of years old, handed down for generations from father to son. Each one is unique, a marvel of intricate decorative design.

The loads on the carts often tower high above the drivers' heads; but, as in the case of the cork, they are usually quite light.

When lunchtime comes, the women dish up from a community fire; but there is no community cooking pot here. Each worker has brought his stewpot from home, filled with his wife's own good cooking; during the morning all the pots are kept bubbling hot over the common fire.

When the loads of cork reach market, the bulk of the crop is sold for export. Most of the rest is carved into charming small toys, bottle stoppers with painted heads, and the like. These toys, along with the clay whistles, handmade lace, brightly painted furniture and equally bright pottery of other craftsmen, are sold, as they have been for generations, in many a market place.

Strips of freshly cut cork bark are placed in the sun to dry.

TO THE BULL RING

On the rich flat plains of Ribatejo, to the south of centrally located Lisbon, cattle graze. Among them ride cowboys called "campinos," wearing stocking caps of green and red, the colors of Portugal's flag. In place of lariats, they carry long, iron-tipped lances, and as they ride they keep a keen eye out for the most spirited of the bulls. After each roundup, the bravest and most ferocious are singled out to be trained for the "corrida," the bull ring. For of all Portuguese sports none is so popular and beloved as bullfighting. And nowhere is the special quality of the Portuguese temperament better illustrated than in their manner of fighting the bull.

The difference starts in the early training, when horses are allowed to run free with the bulls. For the horses, too, play an important part in the Portuguese version of the bullfight. In Spanish countries, the horses used in the bull ring are often poor broken creatures. Not so in Portugal. Here the horses are splendid, aristocratic beasts, specially bred of a proud Arabian strain. Their grace and agility are as much admired as the fighting heart of the bull, the graceful swirl of the matador's cape. Their flanks are protected against the bull's sharp horns with padding; for to the Portuguese, skill, grace and agility are the qualities to be applauded, not bloodshed, violence and death.

So the bull is never killed in the bull ring of Portugal. At the moment of climax the "torero" discards his sword and plants instead the "banderillos," two small decorated pointed sticks, in the shoulders of the bull. These signify the symbolic death or conquest of the bull, the triumph of the torero.

Actually, this moment does mark the end of the earthly career of the bull. Having experienced the challenge of fighting a man, he would probably kill the next one he met, so he must be destroyed. But this is done hu-

The cowboys of Portugal keep a sharp eye out for promising young bulls.

manely in a packing house, and he is sold for beef; he has had his moment of glory.

In Portugal the torero is a national hero, as much so as a Big League baseball star in the United States. And it is the dream of every boy in Portugal to become a torero. So wherever bulls are bred, in the moorlands and on the plains, you will find lads practicing with cape and banderillos. At first, one of the boys, wearing a mask with horns, plays the part of the bull. His opponent in the game advances with decorated sticks, jumping and prancing with all earnestness, as if his very life depended upon the outcome. If he shows talent, he will next get a young heifer to practice with. He may go on to the small village corridas. Perhaps he will become a comedy torero, using his agility and skill to make up with laughter for the splendor and pomp which only the large cities can afford.

Though a boy may not become a torero, still there is one time when he may have a chance to face a bull. This is on the great occasion when the bulls are driven through the narrow streets of a town to the corrida.

Young bulls graze peacefully on the rich, flat plain of the south of Portugal.

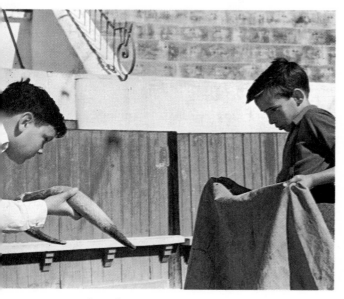

It is the dream of every young Portuguese boy to become a famous "torero."

The toreros of Portugal are its great national heroes and receive great ovations.

The villagers line the streets to watch the fun as the troop of big animals rumbles past.

Once in a while a bull suddenly takes it into his head to leave his group and to challenge some hapless bystander. The wise man will make for the safety of the nearest doorway; but sometimes, with boyhood's dreams of glory lingering in his heart, he capers and gestures, flaunting a snatched-up rag as a cape to taunt the bull. Only when it becomes apparent that he has taken on more than he can handle do the other bystanders distract the animal until he is thoroughly befuddled and any danger is past.

In the ring at last, horses, bulls and men join in an intricately patterned bit of pageantry. The horse has been as carefully trained as the torero to execute the intricate prancing step which is part of the ceremony, for the first charge is made on horseback. The training of the bull has emphasized spirit rather than showmanship, but he is no less majestic in his dignity than the horse.

Perhaps bravest of all the brave in the corrida are the "fercados," who fight the bull with bare hands. Working in a team, they must seize the bull by the horns and twist his head until he is stopped in his tracks. The leader of the fercados goes first; he may grip the bull by the tail with one hand, while clinging fast with the other to one horn. Around and around the enraged animal circles, dragging the fercado with him on the ground. If the man loses his grip, or the bull whirls to charge him, the other fercados leap in with bare hands and capes to distract the animal and save their teammate.

To the pageantry and colorful thrills of bullfighting, demanding valor and gallantry, the Portuguese add a touch of the gentleness and good humor which are also part of the national character. Perhaps the finest of the pageantry is found in Lisbon, the capital, that charming, good-humored city ranged like a pattern of pastel-colored toy blocks over its many hills. Some of the streets are as steep as stairways; but the main avenue of the city since time immemorial has been the broad Tagus River flowing at Lisbon's front door.

It is the Tagus which brings the sea to Lisbon; and it is the sea which has been Portugal's highway to the world and the source of her now-vanished wealth and power. It was from Portugal, at the dawn of the Age of Exploration, that some of the most daring explorers sailed.

In 1488, Bartholomeu Diaz became the first European to sail round the Cape of Good Hope. Eleven years later Vasco da Gama sailed even further and reached India. These two events were probably the most important in Portuguese history, for they opened up the wealth of the Indies to Portugal and were the foundation of its empire.

And one of the greatest of all explorers was the Portuguese navigator Ferdinand Magellan, who was the leader of the first expedition to sail around the world.

There are reminders in Portugal of many influences: ruined Roman cities, Moorish palaces (but for the terrible earthquake of 1755, much of Lisbon's architecture would be Moorish still), Celtic bagpipes in the north, as well as Phoenician-style fishing boats. But the strongest influence in Portugal has surely been the sea, which flows up tidal estuaries into the country's very heart and washes its long, rugged coastline with the wild lashing of surf. Most of the great buildings of Portugal pay homage to the sea in a wealth of decorative designs—ropes and anchors and seashells. And are not her people's simple strength, and proud independence, and timeless satisfaction with old ways a reflection of their long training in learning to live at peace with the ocean at their door?

The fishing village of Nazaré rises on hills overlooking the Atlantic Ocean.

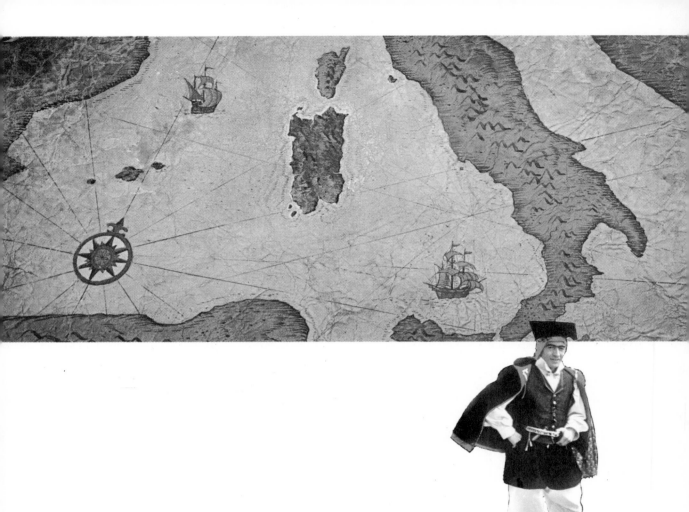

SARDINIA
An Island Apart

CHUGGING about Sardinia's rocky highlands in a miniature train, through wild, desolate scenery, it is impossible not to wonder about the island's lonely and isolated air. The cattle in the rocky hillside pastures, the horses and burros on the dusty mountain roads, even the people we meet are small of size, as if they have been shut away too long from any contact with the big world outside.

Sardinia is centrally enough located, in the western Mediterranean Sea, not far off the coast of Italy. Today it belongs to Italy; but because the island turns a bleak, harborless coast toward the mainland, its people are not really a part of Italian life. In the past Sardinia has fallen prey to many invaders.

A TROUBLED PAST

This rocky island is a natural fortress, yet it never has been able to defend itself, due principally to lack of population. In prehistoric times, the island people learned to fear the scrape of enemy keels on their beaches, the bonfires of invaders blazing in the night. So they built themselves, back in the Bronze Age, a system of watch-tower-fortresses which still stand today. These round stone towers, about thirty feet across at the base and diminishing in size as they rise, are called "nuraghis" and their ruins dot the island everywhere. They loom up on rocky mountain peaks; they surmount ridges; they command the views down dramatic gorges and river valleys. The large ones were apparently equipped to withstand siege, often with a well or spring within the walls, with niches at the entrance in which sentries could hide, with stairways leading to platforms or second floors above. Between these large towers stand smaller ones so spaced that signals could be passed along from one tower to the next down the chain.

The population of Sardinia in those days was numerous and sturdy enough to hold off for some hundreds of years parties of seafaring Greeks bent on pillage or even peaceful settlement. It was only in 500 B.C. that the island fell to the first of the great conquests, by the Carthaginians. Carthage was then a rich and powerful young city of traders on the North African coast; it held the island of Sardinia until the power of Rome eclipsed that of Carthage in the Mediterranean world. Then Sardinia passed to the new victor, supplying many shiploads of corn for the armies and the city people of Rome. As in many lands, Rome built great cities here;

A shepherd of Sardinia guards his flock on the island's steep and rugged hills.

one of these can still be seen off the coast, lying in ruins at the bottom of the sea, its broken pillars wavering in the eerie light, its mosaic floors glowing dimly, half covered by sand.

After the power of Rome had dwindled, the Saracens came to Sardinia, bringing Moslem ways. Moorish influences are still to be seen, and more clearly to be heard in the mournful music of the land.

The Crusades brought an end of Moorish efforts to colonize the little island. But the Crusades did not bring peace to Sardinia. For now the city-states of Italy were growing in power, and Genoa and Pisa both reached out to add the island to their rule. Spanish Aragon owned it for a while and even Austria, before Sardinia was granted in 1770 to the Italian dukes of Savoy.

But long before this the Sardinian people, grown wary and weary of invaders, had retired to mountain villages for survival, full of hatred for all authority. In this bleak mountain world, cut off from outside contacts, small groups became ingrown and separated from their neighbors. Bitter blood feuds developed among the brooding people. And whole villages, because of desperate poverty, made their living by banditry until fairly recent years.

But there is hospitality in these hills, the simple, warm-hearted hospitality born of loneliness; and travelers find a heart-felt welcome though the people may have little indeed of worldly goods to share.

MOUNTAIN CROPS

In Sardinia, winds have sculptured the island rocks, and the topsoil between them is so thin that only by patient and careful scratching with sticks can it be tilled here and there for a crop. Much of the topsoil was lost with the forests, ravished by speculators

Sardinia's grain crop is always scant and must be carefully harvested to avoid loss.

who slashed down the trees with savage thoroughness, burning the wood for charcoal to sell. Today there are only scattered groves of cork trees, some glowing red where the bark has been newly stripped; the pale gray-green of olive groves as stooped and weathered as the rocks themselves; some oranges, prickly pears, chestnuts, oaks and pines—and mile after mile of bare and dusty upland rock.

A scant crop of barley growing among these rocks is reaped as gently as the picking of flowers. For each precious grain must be preserved if the farmers are to have a crop worthy of the name.

There is another and more unusual mountain harvest—chestnuts. Someone, usually a grown man, climbs the chestnut tree and shakes the stout limbs one by one to send the nut burs tumbling to the ground. Boys and girls scamper, armed with tongs or pairs of sticks, picking up the prickly nuts by the apron or basketful. The outer shells are broken with stones or other hard objects and the nuts are stored away to serve as a vegetable throughout the lean and chilly winter.

BARLEY TO BREAD

As for the barley, it is taken to the mill for grinding into flour. The mill is a simple one, often in a home; and in its structure and the set of the stones it is usually quite like those which, we know from the ruins of Pompeii, were in use two thousand years ago. There

Unbaked clay jars are waiting their turn to go into the kiln at the pottery of Oristano.

A wedding feast in Sardinia calls for the most elaborate and beautiful pastries.

may be a water wheel of brushwood with earthen pots tied on to provide the power for the mill; there may be a small, patient, blindfolded donkey ambling around and around and around to turn the grinding stone. In a dozen years of work, such a burro may travel about 5,000 miles, or sixteen times around the island, without ever leaving home. At lunch time, off comes his blindfold and on goes his nosebag. When he has finished eating on goes the blindfold again, and without any signal the burro starts his patient circling once more.

A whole morning's work in a home mill will produce about five pounds of flour; and the flour will soon be put to use. All the steps in the process, from barley head to loaf of bread, may take place in the same room. Here the grain is sorted and cleaned, ground into flour, sifted into a large wooden pan, blended with liquid and mixed by hand, and readied for the oven. The baking is usually done by professional bakers who visit each home in the village, doing up a week's supply at a time. The baker's pay is a share of the bread itself, patted into big, round flat, unleavened loaves.

These loaves are called "carta da musica," or "music paper," because of their yellowish color and parchment-like appearance. They are very practical in households where dishes and utensils are few, for when the flat loaf has been split open other food can be piled upon the bread itself in place of a plate for each diner. But actually other foods are scarce; bread itself is the principal nourishment of the island's many poor.

Not all the baking is plain. Sardinians love fancy confections, especially for special feasts. These pastries are often marvels of elaborate shape and jewel-like decoration. They, too, are the work of professional bakers, and they are truly works of art, with birds and hearts and fringe-petaled flowers of pastry decorating them in infinite variety.

WEDDING BELLS

Elaborate pastries are not of course a part of the daily diet. The most elegant of them are made for weddings. A wedding is a very important occasion indeed, for as is true with most isolated mountain peoples, the respect for women is unusually high here, and old customs are clung to with the deep devotion born of mistrust of change. So around a wedding most of all cling the old, familiar ways, centuries old.

Almost anywhere in the world, where there's a wedding there is music, and Sardinia is no exception. Here the music is often from pipes distantly related to Scottish bagpipes, though without the bags. It is in this haunting music that we hear the voices of Africa and Spain. These are not the gay, lilting melodies of Italy, but something closer to the minor-keyed wailing music of the Arabs and Moors. It is not surprising that this should be true, for there are villages in Sardinia, along the seacoasts, which are like bits of pure North Africa, and others which are like transplanted villages of Spain.

The bride, wearing her elaborately jeweled wedding gown, listens to the music.

All the townspeople join in the wedding celebration as a street musician plays.

But to return to the wedding—the pipes are joined by an accordion, and soon voices rise in song. The friends of the groom serenade the bride in flowery terms: "It is wonderful to see you so lovely. To the heavens I address this prayer: May you both live in peace, like peaceful angels." Then the groom offers a solo. And the bridesmaids warble something like this: "It was written that you should be together, although destiny has allowed your eyes to meet but once."

All the guests stop by for a look at the wedding gifts, laid out on the marriage bed; they sample the wedding foods with which the table is laden. For such a feast there may be lamb or wild boar, marinated in wine and baked in an out-of-door oven in the courtyard. There will be some of the local wines, and special wedding pastries.

But the heart and life of the wedding celebration is in the dancing which sometimes lasts several days. Round and round, with loose-linked arms, the dancers shuffle, around and back. Hour after hour they keep it up; and while to an onlooker the dancing may look dull, it evidently gives the greatest pleasure to those who take part.

FESTIVALS

Like all hard-working people, the Sardinians make the most of their holidays and festivals. Here the saints are held in high esteem, and their special days are set aside for appropriate celebration. Families may horde food for months against a special feast. And if the favorite village of the saint is at some distance, the whole family will travel to town in a two-wheeled ox cart to camp there through the festival.

They make quite a picture as they trundle down the mountain road, to the screeching of the wagon's solid wheels. Over the cart an awning has been spread; to each side is fastened a kitchen chair, a seat of honor for the wife and some other fortunate soul who will jounce along suspended above the road. The rest of the family rides inside the cart, huddled on mattresses among the clutter of cooking pots, cheeses, bread, potatoes and fresh-killed lamb or kids for the feast. There must also be wax candles to be lighted in the church before the shrine of the saint.

Through the dust and heat of summer, through a countryside burned dry, the country carts rumble down to town. And even the poorest village, fragrant from its population of goats, takes on a gay and colorful air during a festival. There's more than a little excitement, too, with processions featuring the statues of the saint, and sometimes bareback horse races down the main street.

One festival which draws people from all over the island is called the "Ardia." It is a re-enactment of an incident involving a troop of Sardinian cavalry who rescued the banner of the emperor Constantine in an ancient battle at the gates of Rome. The horsemen representing the heroic cavalry gather on a hill above the church, with their banner proudly held high. Below mass the men on foot who plan to wrest the banner away— if they can. Then follows such a riding at

A fisherman will make a long journey by ox cart to attend his home village's festival.

Most Sardinian festivals feature street processions honoring the town's saint.

This young man is the winner of the exciting horse race called the "Capo Ardia."

the gallop, such a milling and racing and plunging through gates and leaping over walls that it is impossible for an outsider to follow the action clearly. But the horsemen ride nine times around the church before the melee is done. There are shoutings and shootings off of guns; there is racing and chasing; horses collide. And a fine time is had by all.

FESTIVAL FINERY

Much of the color of these festivals is contributed by the costumes the villagers proudly display. So intricate is the handwork on these costumes that many months of labor may be involved in one, and a village woman may wear for the occasion several hundred dollars' worth of finery.

In many villages, the old-time costumes are going out of style for everyday wear, but at festival time they reappear, and one fa-

A Sardinian woman's festival costume indicates her home village.

With a great deal of shouting and shooting of guns, the riders circle the town church.

miliar with the island can tell the home village of any woman by the dress she wears. Deep red and scarlet, fast-dyed with berry juices, are popular colors, especially for handwoven skirts of the native wool. The skirts are full-pleated and often embroidered; a white blouse is a part of the dress, and

there may be a jacket, often embroidered in vivid shades of yellow and blue.

Widows wear the same style made up in all-black. In certain villages, even the girls wear black; and they may wear pleated wimples about their lower faces, harking back to olden times, perhaps to Moorish days when women were veiled.

For men, too, there is a wide variety of costumes; here we see green corduroy suits with high black boots; in another village, white shirts with black or red waistcoats and jackets. Some wear short, stiff kilts of black wool with a band drawn between the legs; others have short linen trousers with black wool leggings and coin-buttoned waistcoats topped with black sheepskin coats.

For headgear, the typical Sardinian topping is a black "stocking cap" about a foot and a half long, hanging down on one side; countrymen have found the tail a convenient storage spot for small odds and ends or even a bit of lunch. And on a long trip from village to village, a bite of bread tucked away close at hand is a comforting thing to have.

SHEEP IN THE FOLD

High among the granite peaks, you may happen upon an occasional cone-shaped, thatched-roofed hut. Such a hut is a sign of a sheep fold; it is a shepherd's shelter.

In the most remote areas of the island, you may even come upon a few wild sheep—"mufloni," they are called. These are the original inhabitants of the mountains, and once they were very plentiful. Hunters have slashed their numbers so severely that today they are rarely seen, and the few that remain are protected by law. But their tamed cousins, the domestic flocks, are everywhere to be found and are indispensable to the Sardinians. The wool, the meat, the milk, butter and cheese these sheep provide go far to-

Dancers from a distant village await their turn to perform in a Sardinian festival.

Many months of skilled handiwork may be involved in making one festival costume.

The women of certain Sardinian villages wear these bright-colored caps about the house.

Fresh-sheared wool is soaked in a pot filled with hot water to remove some of the oil.

The wool is then scrubbed on the rocks in the cool water of a nearby stream.

Then the water is squeezed from the wool, and it is loaded into bags and carried home.

ward providing the islanders' simple livelihood.

Each morning and evening the sheep are gathered for milking. Some of the milk is drunk; some is churned into butter; much of it is converted into cheese—the ripe, flavorful sheep's milk cheese called "pecorino."

This cheesemaking is a strong-smelling process, often carried on out in the field. The month of May, when the pastures are fresh and green, is considered a good time for cheesemaking. The stomach of a fresh-killed lamb, containing milk mixed with digestive juices, makes a culture for the cheese. Meanwhile, chunks of fresh lamb roasted on a spit make a hearty treat for the cheesemakers.

The cheese, of either sheep or goat's milk, is worked by hand. Olive oil and other ingredients are often added to it in the pan and give the cheese a rather strong, primitive flavor. It ages until September, and is ready for marketing in the winter.

Wool is of course an important product of the flocks. The sheep are sheared in the field, then the women take the wool and soak it, first in a large pot of warm water, then in the cool shallows of a nearby stream, scrubbing it on the rocks. This is to remove some of the oil, but by no means all; for this wool is to be woven into a strong, rough, hairy fabric called "orbace," one of whose great attributes is that it is almost water-proof, thanks to its natural oils.

When the women have squeezed the water from the wool, they stuff it into bags, load the sacks onto their small, sturdy horses, and start for the village and home. If they have no horses, nor tiny burros, the women carry the sacks themselves, as they carry in season sacks of grain, loads of wood or young lambs. It is no wonder that the country women of Sardinia, handsome and graceful in their youth, soon age, with heavy joints and stooped, bent backs.

The rough wool is carded with old-fashioned combs to make it ready for spinning.

CLOTH FROM THE LOOM

At home in the hillside villages, the women card the wool and spin it into balls of yarn; then, in preparation for the loom, they stretch the long threads down the village street as they walk, single file, back and forth. Of course before they can weave they must gather it up again, winding it in great hanks around sticks.

Many of their looms are a hundred or more years old; and the looms' simple design goes back thousands of years. A simple shuttle darts through the warp threads and with a downward pull on the cross bar the sley forces the weft into place. To the rasp and the creak and the rhythm of the loom, the weaving women sing a melancholy tune. But their fabric may be heartily cheerful in color; it may be for a bright, heavy carpet or carpet bag, it may be planned for sturdy everyday aprons and skirts, or it may be a lighter and finer quality for an elegant festival dress.

But when the cloth comes from the loom, the work is by no means done. The material must be stomped and worked with the feet for many hours, to give it flexibility.

The simple design of these home looms goes back thousands of years. Many are very old.

And then there is the job of sewing. Sardinian women pride themselves on needle work both intricate and artistic, and very exactly done. And when we see a finished costume, we agree that their pride is justified.

These Sardinian boys are learning to handle the big oxen on the threshing floor.

Long tuna nets are carried down to the beach in preparation for the great fishing enterprise.

MEN'S WORK

And how are the men occupying themselves while the women are busy with the spindle, loom and needle? Some of them are out watching the flocks, some of them are tending the crops, some are stripping the cork trees of bark or hacking blocks of limestone from the island's quarries, or weaving sturdy baskets out of reeds. Each village has a different specialty.

And since Sardinia is an island place, some of the people draw their livelihood from the waters round about. Actually, the Sardinians themselves have little taste for the sea. It is mainly Genoese and other Italian seafaring folk who man the island's fishing industry, bringing in lobster and sardines for local eating; and at spawning time, when schools pass the island in a steady stream, the fishermen bring in the "tunny" or giant tuna.

Preparations for this biggest fishing enterprise are begun in late March and continue all through April and most of May. Under the direction of a chief called the "rais," the tuna fishing team checks the fitness of the boats, coils hundreds of feet of rope, and strings up the nets for mending.

The nets seem hardly strong enough to hold a tuna, which may weigh close to a thousand pounds, and actually they are not intended to. But the big fish are easily deflected from their course, and the nets, laid out to form long under-water corridors, serve to guide them to a final enclosure.

When all is ready, the big rope is laid out, to which the nets are attached. The rais is in the lead boat for the net laying. Though everyone works early and late, he works hardest of all, for a successful catch depends in large part upon his judgment and ability.

When the guide rope is finally in place, it stretches out two miles from the shore; and then the laying of the nets begins. Two boats work out, one on each side, following the rope lines as they let down the nets. Just as everything seems ready, a final inspection tour shows a swordfish threshing about in the net. His sword has ripped holes in the giant snare, and these must be hastily mended with twine before the start of the run.

Now begins the watching and waiting—for the tuna to pass below the boats. On top of the ropes, where they meet at right angles, a cross is placed; and this cross marks the entrance to the final enclosure, which is called "the chamber of death."

Lures are tossed into the water to bring the fish closer to the surface. Up they come, visible as dark spots against the foaming water—first one, then a few, then a dark, swirling blanket just below the surface, between the ropes, swimming all unknowing into the ominous "chamber of death."

When enough of the tuna have entered the chamber, the rais gives a signal; the boatmen man their oars and the boats gather for the first "mattanza," or kill. About the

The Sardinian fishermen are harpooning the big tuna trapped in the "chamber of death."

enclosure they form a square, with one small boat inside. The men stand in their boats, facing the leader inside the square, and for one solemn moment they join bareheaded in prayer. Then the rais, from his small boat out in the center, raises his hands in a signal. The men slam their hats back onto their heads and begin the raising of the nets.

As the winches turn and the ropes shorten, the nets pull the threshing fish to the surface. When the water is filled with fish, the leader lays down his oar as the signal for the next step, and the kill begins. Men line the inner rails of the boats, hooking the big fish and tugging them up to flip them over the rail to the deck. As they give the tuna a last thrust onto the boat, they all lean forward, bending over the rail in order to avoid the lash of the tuna's powerful tail, which could break an arm or even a back.

With the close of day, the run for home is made with heavy-laden boats and light hearts. For prosperity of a simple sort lies ahead for the tuna fishermen when their hazardous work is finally done.

SADNESS AND SUPERSTITION

Into every life some sorrow comes, and the country folk of Sardinia have learned to accept their share of grief and care along with their daily work and joys.

When death comes, as it must, the relatives follow heavy-hearted at a respectful distance as the loved one is brought to the church. Before entering the presence of the dead, each dons the cowl of mourning—a dark shawl—and the endless chants and rhyming laments are led by professional mourners whose classic ritual goes back to ancient times. Thus the villagers pay their respects to death as a part of the natural cycle of life, as normal as birth or breathing.

As the customs of honoring the dead are rooted deep in the past, so are many of the customs of everyday life. Take the treatment of childhood ills, for example. When a child is put to bed with a slight fever, it is the village patriarch who undertakes to cure the ailment with a time-honored trick. His cure may be produced through the magic of sparks struck from steel—a stone against the blade of his knife.

What is the reasoning behind this treatment? Even the old man does not know; the origin of his mystic rite is lost in antiquity. He knows not the "why" but only the "how" of the methods entrusted to him.

Some cures are much stranger. Here is one for an ailment fortunately rare. Sardinians believe that if an owl flies over a child as he leaves the house at night, the child may not

Even the island's children are wary of newcomers from the outside world.

The reed-like "launeddas" provide simple music for a simple way of life.

grow any more. To determine whether this tragedy has struck, the child is measured with a string, first his height and then the width of his arm span. If his reach exceeds his height, it is considered proof that the worst has happened. Steps must then be taken to counteract the evil influence of the owl.

A mystic potion is made, using the string with which the child was measured. Cut into bits, it is blended in a dish with a lock of his hair and a piece of his clothing. A match is struck, a candle lighted; at the candle flame the bit of clothing is ignited, from it the other magical ingredients are set aflame, and soon a bit of black ash is all that remains.

The ashes are mixed with black coffee which, with the proper incantations, is administered to the sputtering, resisting boy. And if all goes well, right will win out, and the boy will grow to manhood and full size despite the evil night-spell of the owl.

He will grow to manhood, marry and have a family; he will celebrate at the village festivals, perhaps light a candle now and then in the church, though most of the church-going he will leave to the women folk. He will work all his days to earn a simple livelihood, spicing his hardships with a bit of good talk and song. And in so doing he will carry on for another generation a pattern of life that is simple and heart-warming in its familiarity, the pattern of simple island life of the rugged and resourceful people of Sardinia.

MOROCCO

The Blue Men

MOTIONLESS as a statue in the folds of his blue cloak stands the Moor. In the words of Saint-Exupéry, "he does not defend his liberty, for in the desert one is always free, nor does he defend visible treasures, for the desert is bare; but he defends a secret realm."

This realm lies in South Morocco, between the double walls of the Atlas and Anti-Atlas mountains, protected on the west by a coast so inhospitable and treacherous that in former times only shipwrecked mariners landed there, while away to the south and east rolls the limitless Sahara Desert. Here live more than thirty or forty thousand—no one knows precisely how many, since civil government has not yet penetrated here—descendants of Arab conquerors, the last great nomads.

THE BLUE MEN

Truly great nomads, these. For while the more familiar nomad peoples keep within a certain distance of oases and centers where they can find the essentials of life, these tribes take for their empire the entire desert. To sell their camels (their only real goods) in Tindouf, Goulimine, and even in Marrakech, and to buy their provisions of barley, dates, sugar and tea, they sometimes come up from Mauritania, far to the south in French West Africa—for boundaries mean little to them. In four or five weeks they cover hundreds, even thousands of miles. Then they return to

The Blue Man, one of the world's last nomads, values his independence more than any comforts the modern world can provide.

their grazing lands in the south before setting out again on a new voyage.

The great endurance tests they conduct today in their marches are reminders of the great raids of the old days, more romantic and also more cruel, which they used to conduct against caravans and villages for purposes of plunder. For pillage and plunder were the traditional occupations of these haughty and austere warriors.

Lost seamen, captured by these pirates of the desert to be sold as slaves and redeemed at last for ransom, were the first to reveal to the world the existence of these men, boisterous and insolent, rude and independent, rebelliously contemptuous of our modern "progress," sometimes cruel when the struggle for life enters the game, but with a child-like openheartedness and readiness to laugh.

The eternal search for a distant oasis leads the Blue Man onward in the desert.

ROBES OF BLUE

This strange color, which is not really a racial characteristic, is nevertheless the color of their skin. Slowly, when the great explorers of the Sahara made their first contacts with these curious people, an explanation of the mystery was found: the blue is the color of their clothing, and the clothing stains their skin.

Contrary to the Arab, who shaves his head, the Blue Man keeps all his hair, trimming it only on the cheeks and the nape of the neck. This imposing black mane, which gives him a rather wild, fierce air, he hides in part under a sort of turban, a strip of cotton several yards long, rolled and twisted, which serves at the same time as tie and scarf. But it serves other uses as well; when the Blue Man does not wear it on his head, he uses it in place of a rope, a veil, a pouch or a belt, and at night as a pillow.

On his face, bronzed by the sun and blued by the indigo dye, he wears a beard. The beard is a symbol. In former times, he who swore to seek vengeance for some offense would smear his beard with blood. Today, in speaking of a man who has lost everything, one sketches the gesture of tearing out his beard. And in olden times, in certain tribes,

the punishments inflicted by the group on the chief of a family for perjury or betrayal were, in order of increasing severity, to burn his tent, to shave the head of his wife, or finally to cut his beard—a chastisement so grave that it was almost never applied.

On his shoulders and torso the Blue Man wears a full cotton shirt; often he wears several, one on top of the other, for the best protection against the heat of the desert is to be well covered. His trousers are short, and wide at the bottom. He footwear is a leather sole held on by a thong passing between the great toe and the next, permitting him to slip it off quickly; for when the sand is not too hot, the nomad prefers to walk barefoot.

Both shirt and turban are blue—a violet-blue which is really indigo. This dye in former times came from Arabia. Today the blue cotton fabrics are prosaically manufac-

A never-ending journey with his camels is the Blue Man's mode of life.

The women of these tribes spend many leisure hours on elaborate hairdressing.

is not actually practiced. Beyond the family, all those who share a common ancestor are grouped together, and there are subdivisions of the tribe and the tribe itself. A "sheikh," meaning "old one," is the head of a subdivision; a "said," or chief, always of an old family, heads the tribe. He does not rule by force, but clings above all to his right to have his power passed down at his death to another member of his family. When a said dies, one of his relatives, generally aged, always greatly respected, will be chosen to take his place by the council of the elders, the "djemaa."

tured in Great Britain and sent out from Nigeria to the points where the nomads touch the edge of the desert. But their capacity for coloring the skin has been retained, for the reason these nomads like blue so much is not purely aesthetic. The indigo dye also offers a remarkable protection against the sun, and when they have had very hot rays beating down upon them, for a long time, the Blue Men rub their faces, limbs and all the exposed parts of their bodies with their turbans or shirts.

As for the women, they wear, like the men, pantaloons and shirts, but they drape themselves on the outside in robes made of two pieces of blue cotton cloth. They do not cover their faces with the traditional veil, which is not suitable for the demands of their wandering life. And their hair is of great importance to them. Scarcely a week goes by in which the women do not get together for a hairdressing session at which they spend untold hours dressing one another's hair in dozens of tight little braids.

These then are the men and women whose caravan we are going to follow. The basic unit of their society is the tent, housing a man, his wife and children and sometimes the grandparents. Polygamy is permitted, but

PREPARATIONS FOR A JOURNEY

The territory in which the Blue Men have developed is immense. All of the western Sahara, from South Morocco to Senegal, Rio de Oro, and Mauritania in the south, is their domain. But the big moves cannot be accomplished with more than a small number—

With the exception of hairdressing sessions the lives of these women offer few diversions.

The men of the camp make quite a ceremony of drinking tea, their principal beverage.

On the long desert journeys of the Blue Men, rest stops are essential.

The shade of the tent roof provides welcome shelter from the blazing sun.

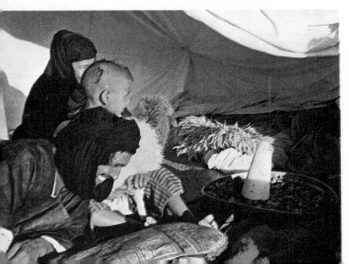

thirty or forty persons, perhaps fifteen tents and of course the camels.

The flocks of goats will be left in the care of guardian herdsmen in the grazing lands of the south, whose zones have been jealously divided among the tribes since ancestral times. The caravan departs from Attar, at the edge of Mauritania, headed toward the vicinity of Tindouf, more than six hundred miles away. Tindouf has become a market town, so they will take their camels there to sell; if the camels are not all sold there, the Blue Men will take them across the Atlas Mountains to the market at Marrakech.

For the long trip, it is not practical to load the camels down with heavy tents for comfort. The tents must be light, and easy to set up and to take down. They are roofed with strips of goats' wool or camels' hair fabric, woven by the women on rough looms which are set up on the ground. Only the rich nomads use in addition a strip of white fabric to form a double roof.

The tents are supported in the middle by wooden stakes. Some other pegs made of roots of "talha"—a thorny shrub from whose resin gum arabic comes—with long ropes attached, pin the tent to the ground, and give a certain flexibility to the arrangement. They are effective in holding against the wind, which blows in such strong gusts that tents are kept very flat as protection against it.

When suddenly the sky takes on a yellow color, though, the nomads know that no tent pins can hold, for the "chergui" soon begins to blow—that terrible wind from the southeast. It stirs up sandstorms which wither and smother everything in their path, and sometimes last up to nine days. Then the only refuge is to throw the central post to the ground, flattening the tent cloth, and to crouch on the earth under the shelter of the heavy fabric, awaiting the worst.

The tent is divided in two: the side of the women, with simple cooking and housekeeping equipment, and the side of the men, with the necessities for hospitality—that is to say, the tea pot and accessories for serving tea: glasses, a loaf of sugar, and a small two-headed hammer made of engraved copper and used for cracking the sugar.

Green tea is actually the principal beverage of the nomads. Its preparation follows a ritual which demands patience and care. It is the man, most often, who is in charge, and this post is always an honor. The tea—which replaced coffee during a production crisis in Brazil—is, like the cotton fabric, furnished by British Nigeria. It comes from China or Ceylon, but has undergone a special treatment and is as sweet as syrup. They often use the expression "to drink sugar" instead of "to drink tea." And the quantities they drink, at least in times of prosperity when there is no shortage of water, are extraordinary. An old saying is evidence: "One glass is nothing, two is poor, three is the rule, four is notional, five forbidden (khamssa, the number five, is in fact bad luck), six is better than three."

WOMEN'S WORK

Let us go to the other side of the tent, that of the women. There they watch the fireplace, built of some collected stones, on which the one-family cooking pot rests permanently. Keeping up the fire is difficult, for wood is scarce in the desert stretches which the Blue Men cross. All along the way the women gather dead branches, and when they are totally lacking, dried camel dung serves as fuel.

The drudgery of woodgathering, caring for the goats, weaving and repairing of the tent and packing and unpacking it at each stop, along with other tasks of homemaking, leaves the women little time for social life. Existence is hard for the nomads; a woman of twenty years is already faded, a man of

The striking of the tents after an encampment is one of the women's many hard tasks.

Preparation for the simple meals is not difficult, as they are necessarily frugal.

Dates are the favorite sweet meats, and one of the important foods, of the Blue Men.

forty years is often an old man. Often under-nourishment speeds the aging process, for the meals the women prepare must of necessity be very frugal. Rarely is there meat; more often the main dish is a simple "dchicha," with a base of barley boiled and mixed with oil. And there is usually milk. The women milk not only the camels but some few goats which have been brought along to be kept in a paddock at the side of the tent, protected from jackals by a fence of talha thorns.

A proverb of the Blue Men says: "He who has no milk in his home has nothing. He who has no milk has no friends."

Milk, especially that of the camels, may be the only food of the tribe when the provisions of grain and of dates are exhausted. It is milk which they present to the stranger who approaches the tent; for milk forms a bond between those who have partaken of it together, and this bond is considered to be

The contempt of the camels for their masters is legendary, and quite true.

as strong as that of blood. Then there is butter, made by shaking the milk for some hours in a goatskin. This is a highly valued food, and it is the custom for young married women to smear the wood of their tent posts with butter in an attempt to win prosperity for their future home.

THE CAMELS

All around the camp, the hobbled camels are grazing, if you can call the dry, sparse tufts poking up among the stones pasture. Then there are also the talha bushes, whose branches, which seem to us like barbed wire, the camels lick with delight. For camels, fortunately, are content with meager nourishment.

Much mystery surrounds the origin of the single-humped African camel, properly called the dromedary. It is generally thought that he is descended from an ancient Indian line, and that he arrived in Syria and Arabia about the beginning of the Christian era. He is lighter, longer-legged, and swifter than the Asian camel, with shorter, woolier hair. His great height and majestic appearance make him a true lord of the desert.

The camel lives twenty-five years if he works, almost double that if he is free. His reputation for going without drinking is in large part a legend. It is only at rest and in a region where he can find grass—real green grass—that he is able to go several weeks without drinking, for the greens themselves supply him with water he needs. When grass is plentiful, his hump inflates and hardens, for it is there that he accumulates his reserves. But when he is working, and during the hot season, the hump softens, melts away and disappears. Then he will not be able to go more than four days without water; and, at a stop, in a single day he will drink eighty to a hundred quarts.

The wives and children of chiefs ride in litters high on the backs of the camels.

With some food and sufficient water, he is capable of covering, with three hundred pounds on his back, tens of miles a day, at the pace of a man on foot—but never cheerfully. Bored, scornful of his masters, to whom he never becomes attached, he seems to find his work repugnant; and when he is loaded down he gives great groans, deep and raucous. That done, he resigns himself to his task. And it is with the same resignation that this strange animal, worn out at last with having walked, heavily loaded, for a quarter century under the same sky, lays himself down at last on the sand to die.

DEPARTURE

The hour of the great departure has arrived. For some weeks the men, in the shade of the tents, have been discussing the route of the caravan. The chief of the tribe and the chiefs of the families have consulted together, for a voyage of several hundred miles is a difficult enterprise for which preparations

must be made with care. It is necessary to have landmarks for the halts, and to make camp at points where there is known to be water, either those wells of the Sahara which are simply holes flush with the soil, past which strangers might ride without noticing anything, or those rare oases which are like islands in the midst of the desert.

For men as for beasts, the great problem of the journey, on which the route, even the organization, of the caravan depends, is the problem of water. The rains are of extreme violence and can bring out in a few hours miraculous tufts of green grass; but their arrival can also be delayed as much as a year or more. Here under the blazing sun a man cannot live more than eight hours without water. The "guerba," the goatskin in which the nomads carry their water supply, must be kept filled. This guerba, made of an entire skin turned inside out, tanned with tar and rancid butter, is a splendid piece of typically Saharan equipment. Pliable, tough, waterproof, it holds twenty to twenty-five quarts of water, keeping it at a certain temperature, thanks to slow evaporation. It is the canteen of the desert.

Now it is morning. The nomad could not name the hour, for he does not mark the hours off, having no need to. He can read the sun with almost the precision with which we read our watch faces.

The camel drivers prepare their beasts while the women are striking the tents, uprooting the posts and packing the supplies. The most precious objects—clothing, jewels, tea, sugar, grain and dates—are stowed in the "tissoufra," a great cover for provisions made of goatskin and decorated with geometric designs. The tent and its posts make up one camel's load. The sacks are packed on other beasts.

On still other camels, litters are rigged up, in which the wives and children of the chiefs ride; these have skeletons of wood covered

The desert has varied scenery; this wind-rippled sand is typical of the Sahara.

The caravan moves patiently and slowly across the long, hot, weary miles.

Within sight of an oasis, the Blue Men camp in anticipation of their first market day.

with cloth, which protects their passengers against the rays of the sun. In their height and decoration one can measure the wealth of the chief and his affection for his wife. The camels which are to be sold in the market carry no loads, for their owners want them to appear strong and healthy to their prospective buyers.

OASIS

Seen on the horizon, beyond the dune there, the first palm appears. It is the oasis! Soon we see the square walls of the "ksar," a village once fortified against the attacks of these same Blue Men who are arriving today. At the approach of the caravan, the villagers hurry inside the walls. The raids of olden times have left their mark, so that even now when an unknown tribe arrives, the villagers entrench themselves behind their walls. But the uneasiness is short-lived, for these Blue Men are not unknown to the villagers. These are their protectors, with whom they have signed a pact.

This strange agreement, a souvenir of the old raiding days, is a sort of primitive "protection racket." In consideration of a "tax of brotherhood," which is paid in grain and dates, the stay-at-home villagers are assured against raids and pillage of the sort which was common in the old days. There is only one absolute rule: that in order to avoid conflict, the villagers must go into their homes and the gates of the town must be closed at the fall of night. Only the watchman is permitted to spend the night in the oasis among the barley fields. And he is a Blue Man who stays at the oasis permanently.

This is the first big port of call of the voyage. It is the first meeting place between the nomads of the desert and that other world of the settled mountain folk.

Here the beasts stop and kneel for unloading. And, as always, the women commence to busy themselves raising the tents, the talhas of the desert as usual providing the necessary pins for fastening up a piece of cloth to close them snugly at the back. The evening meal will be more abundant than those of the preceding days. Dates reappear on the menu and the tea will be perfumed with mint.

The caravan has established its encampment on the desert near one of the fortified villages which surround the oasis. Their makeshift houses of sun-dried mud are spaced a bit openly for better protection against the heat. Between them, narrow streets lead back into a maze of shadowy passageways where the sun never penetrates.

In these villages the slave market used to be held, for this is the point where the great caravans used to come up from the Sudan with their cargoes of chained Negroes. Today the oasis has become a provisioning center for the nomads in dates, grain, tea, sugar, oil and cloth; and the people of the neighboring villages sometimes come shopping for camels.

These fortified villages are inhabited by Berbers, agricultural people with regular fea-

The fortified walls of the "ksar" were built as a protection against the Blue Men.

tures, their hair generally brown, sometimes blond. They are big, fierce, independent men. Doing the rough farmwork are others, who have thick lips, flat noses and very dark skin. They are called "haratin," which means laborers; they are mostly descendants of Sudanese slaves of olden times.

THE PALM OF ALLAH

"Allah, give your blessing
To our prophet Mohammed.
Allah, give him greetings.
Palm trees, you are the palms of Allah!"

This chant, offered by a hundred voices, rises up from the palm groves from the beginning of day until the setting of the sun. The voices are those of the villagers, perched in the trees, gripping the trunks with bare hands and feet, and chanting while they accomplish a delicate operation most essential to the whole life of the oasis: introducing some sprigs of pollen into the female blossoms to fertilize the palm.

One cannot depend on nature alone for the fertilization of these trees which are the blessing of the Sahara. Nor can one risk letting them languish. For at the same time that they are providing the shade so necessary to animal and vegetable, they provide fruit which makes up the principal food supply of the people of South Morocco; fibers from which mats are woven and baskets of all sorts are fashioned; hairy floss from which rope is made; and wood from which comes beams for the houses.

The date palm lives with its head in the fire; but it must have its feet in the water. It demands at the same time hot sun and humid soil. As is typical in this world of the desert, water is the indispensable element of its life. This is why the master of the water

The waters of the oasis feed and keep alive the vitally important "palms of Allah."

Man power as well as animal power is used to raise the water from the deep oasis wells.

is a person of great importance in the oasis.

Usually it is a spring which assures the irrigation of the palms. The water comes to the parcels of cultivated soil down canals which flow between the walls of the fields. It is up to the master of the water to distribute this water among all the villagers. To do this, a system of "irrigation turns" is set up. This is how it works: each date grower has the right to the whole flow of the spring for a certain time. The time is measured by an old device like the hourglass, with a copper pan pierced through the middle by a small hole. The pan is placed in a large vessel of water. It fills up little by little and sinks slowly to the bottom. The time it takes to fill is the unit of time of one "turn at the water." Each grower inherits or buys the number of turns to which he has the right.

Each time the pan fills, the master of the water makes a knot in a palm frond. When the number of knots assigned to a grower is completed, the master gives forth a strident cry which permits no discussion; the man closes his gate and the turn at the water passes on to the next.

In other corners of the oasis one also finds some wells. They differ in the depth of the water. The most usual equipment is the well pulley, whose turning is accompanied by a groaning and creaking deep inside, which is one of the most characteristic sounds of the Sahara palm grove. There is a rude wooden crank that turns the pulley. A long rope passes over this, bound at one end to the neck of a goatskin bottle, at the other to a man or animal traveling around a path equal to the depth of the well. When he comes to the end of the path, the leather bottle, arriving at the mouth of the well, automatically empties itself. And this maneuver is repeated hundreds of times every day.

These pollen-laden sprigs will be used in the delicate task of fertilizing the date palm.

The haughty camel grudgingly permits himself to be hitched to a plow.

THE VILLAGE MARKET

In the palm grove today, there is the big annual market which is held in the spring, just after the planting of the grain. It lasts officially two or three days, but actually goes on for a whole week, for the Berbers of the Atlas Mountains and these nomads who have just arrived from the desert always stay on at the oasis a little longer than planned.

The Berbers have brought green tea, sugar loaves, barley, cotton goods and carpets. They will trade for shells from the Sudan, ostrich fat, leather goods, and camels.

The camel market is the most important and picturesque. On the market grounds the beasts walk freely, perhaps as many as a thousand of them, under the watchful eye of their masters. The buyer chooses his camel; but more than that he has to catch it, placing, as a sign of ownership, a cord through its nostrils. This is not an easy matter, for the camel, not a bit sociable, refuses to let anyone approach him.

The capture is a real rodeo. Like cowboys, the buyers are armed with lassos. But instead of throwing them into the air, they place the ropes on the ground and several men try to drive the camels toward the circles formed by the knotted loops. When a camel puts one of his feet in the circle, the buyer pulls hard on the rope while others hurl themselves at the camel to throw him to the ground. In the general confusion, one ties the cord to his leg, another puts a line through his nostrils, and this is the only way the new master manages to lead his new property away.

FESTIVALS

In all the neighboring villages, the settled folk are having a festival. In one it is a ceremony in honor of a local saint. All the men and male children (if you ask a desert man how many children he has, he counts only the boys) gather in the village square for a common meal. Each family has brought its dish under a cone-shaped cover. Soon the square is decked with several hundred of these platters: sheets of pastry covered with minced pigeon meat, legumes and raisins, sauces, patties of barley meal. Water is the only beverage, for the Koran forbids alcohol, and tea is not served until the end.

At a signal given by the religious chief in charge, the men take their places and the feast proceeds. The meal ends with a collective prayer, and then the men form a

A tribe of Berbers, the chief native race of North Africa, holds its own celebration.

procession which winds through the streets to a wild, rhythmic beat. At the end of the procession, the men dance to the sound of tambourines.

The festival in another village is in honor of the marriage of the son of a sheikh, in which the whole masculine population of the village takes part. The marriage is celebrated when the student has learned by heart sixty verses of the Koran. Mounted on a mule and holding in his hands a board on which the verses are written, he makes a tour of the village, followed by the Moslem schoolmasters. The mule is led by an old slave dressed in the costume of the Blue Men, as it was the nomads in the old days who brought them up from the Sudan.

In still another village the "haratin," the working people, dance, men and women together. The women, decked in their jewelry of silver, amber and coral, are arranged in one row, the men in another. Tambourines mark the rhythm, the dancers clapping their hands. One man detaches himself; he bows before a woman, who in turn leaves her row. More couples join them and dance in the middle of a circle formed by the audience, all under the spell of the chanting, the clapping of hands and the tambourines. Sometimes the male dancer will place his dagger on the shoulder of his dancing partner as a mark of his special interest in her. The festi-

val ends late in the night and sometimes goes on until the next day.

Nearby, in the camp of the nomads, another festival is taking place. The Blue Men do not take part in the festivities of the settled folk, whom they scorn. These ancient warriors dance the dance of the rifles, or one of the daughters may dance the "guedra," an old dance of the nomads.

The guedra is the family cooking pot. Covered with goatskin, it serves as a drum on which to beat out the rhythm with two sticks. The dancer, entirely hidden under a veil, enters on her knees into the circle of men, who mark time by beating their hands. She is content at first to sway to the rhythm. Then she lets her veil fall and appears, smiling. Her face comes to life, then her torso, then her hands and fingers. She bends forward until her long curled locks touch the mats. Accompanied by singing of grave beauty, she dances by the light of torches and campfire, using her hennaed hands in the meaningful yet mysterious gestures of olden days, until she falls to the ground, exhausted.

Meanwhile the sun has set, and, in the villages, at the exact moment when it disap-

These Berber women, who appear to be standing still, are participating in a dance.

pears beyond the horizon, the muezzin climbs to the minaret and cries out the call to prayer from the four corners of the tower, in a voice so clear and pure that it rolls over the whole stretch of the palm groves like a psalm:

"God is great . . .
There is no other God than Allah . . .
And Mohammed is his Prophet.
Come to prayer . . .
Come to joy. . . ."

The heavens take up the cry. Night, which is more beautiful here than day, wraps itself softly about the nomad camp, where from the distance are heard the clashing sound of tambourines, the cries and the chants.

At dawn the next day the Blue Men break camp. One part of the caravan, loaded with the purchases made in town, will head back to the desert. Another part will take on the

In the center of Marrakech is the open market.

rest of the camels for sale in Marrakech, the capital of the south, encircled by the tall peaks of the Anti-Atlas and the Atlas ranges.

MARRAKECH

Marrakech—where side by side with the old native city rises a European capital with broad avenues, public buildings many stories tall, and superb mansions surrounded by palms—was in olden times the feudal city of the Blue Men.

This city was truly born of the sand, founded in the eleventh century by warriors dressed in blue, with covered faces, who surged in from the sands of the Sahara. Within its famous walls, eight miles long and pierced by nine great gates, Marrakech lives in a perpetual market fair.

"Balek! Balek!" Take care! Watch out! This cry, repeated a thousand times, is that of the horsemen, the porters and the donkey drivers who are trying by any means to push

This vegetable market is one of the many small, separate market areas, called "souks."

The souk of the dyers is hung with bright wools, drying in the intense sunlight.

The ramparts of Marrakech stretch eight miles in length and have nine huge gates.

their way through the crowds of the "souks," those picturesque markets of the city. Each one has its specialty.

Here is the souk, or market, of herbs, which in years of drought are measured out in little handfuls; there, the souk of grains, where one finds farina and such. The souk of wool is frequented by women who hide their faces under veils. In the souk of the dyers you pass under hanks of colored wool, hung up to dry, suspended over the narrow alleyway.

At some distance are the souks of the animals: the market of small animals, kids and lambs, which the buyers carry off on their backs; the souk of the donkeys, whom the buyers always try to mount before purchasing; finally the souk of the camels, where we find the Blue Men deep in their bargaining.

Down in the square, which is the heart of the city, a huge temporary market has been set up, crowded with sellers and sightseers. In the shade of big mats suspended between poles are established the vendors of spices, fruits, amulets, fritters, pocket mirrors, prayer carpets, copperware, rose and carnation petals, pomegranate leaves, snakeskins, whips, slippers, beeswax, pots of honey, fly switches, aspirin, perfumes.

Wandering medicine men put their cupping glasses to work on patients, while the barbers, experts with one hand, clip their clients' hair. Water merchants stroll about ringing their bells. Sellers of whey hand out their glasses to people made thirsty by the torrid heat. Sellers of bread, crouched on the ground, offer their hard loaves, while a public scribe puts himself at the disposal of those who want to send a letter. Some open-air restaurants prepare, for a few francs, a soup or small cubes of meat turned on a greased spit. Beggars are a part of the scene, for one of the seven patrons of Marrakech is the saint of beggars. Often in groups of three or four they call out their chant and hold out their wooden bowls to passers-by.

In the middle of the day some new attractions come to swell the spectacle. Circles form, the crowd gathers. Here is the reader of the Koran, who down the years tells the same story over and over, always with the same success. There is a fire-eater; here, a sword juggler. Over there are little dancers from the mountains who, clad in long robes, keep turning round and round, matching their steps to the rhythm of slight movements of ankles and hips. There are pantomimists, comics, vagabonds from distant lands, like the Sudanese dancers.

Finally, there are the snake charmers, who frantically shake their long, loose black locks while the tambourine whips them on, and the shiny black cobras rise up on their tails and follow their gestures with slow movements of their puffed-up heads. Suddenly one takes a snake right in his hands and holds it up to his face before the panting, eager mob.

The Blue Men, once their camels have been sold, wander for a time, joining briefly the circles of sightseers which form and reform in the midst of incredible racket. But they do not stay long in the midst of this turbulent crowd. Their business completed,

Each day, the Blue Men thank Allah for the great blessing of liberty.

they are ready to leave again for the desert, their desert, to rejoin the rest of the tribe.

The old chief who welcomes them on their return wants to hear their story at length (while under the tent his daughters listen as they arrange their hair). But they all know that the story of this trip is no epoch tale. The desert is not like the desert of old, when every fold of sand was filled with menace, when the night was full of enemies, thoughts of whom made the hearts of the people about the campfire beat faster.

Battles and raiding have long been forbidden by the hated Christians who invaded their solitude, their secret realm. In the twentieth century, beneath the wheels of modern vehicles and the drills of petroleum hunters, their civilization is disappearing.

Yet each morning they turn to Mecca and thank Allah for the blessing of their remaining liberty, that liberty which, in spite of all the pain and hardships, they would not exchange for houses, which they could not carry on their journeys, nor for radios, since the world outside does not exist for them, nor for watches, since it is not their custom to count the time.

A European said one day to a Blue Man: "I have flown in three hours the distance it takes your caravan a month to cross. Even you will admit that this is progress?"

The Blue Man replied, "And the rest of the time, what do you do?"

LAPLAND
People of the Reindeer

Down the rough mountainside thunders an antlered herd. Close on their trail, riding in slim, single-runnered sleds, come the herders and their families, keeping an anxious eye on the lowering clouds behind. These herds are reindeer, numbered by the hundreds; their herders are the Lapps, the nomads of the north—the People of the Reindeer.

High in the frigid zone of Europe, where the Arctic Circle cuts through the northern tips of Norway, Sweden, Finland and Russia, lies Lapland—an area with a people, a language, a culture of its own, but not a nation. In this open, rugged land, with neither highways nor towns, national boundaries are of little importance. The Lapps (the name means "nomads" in Swedish), or Samer, as they call themselves, may wander freely over parts of the four nations listed, wherever their herds lead them; for they are protected by special international agreement. Still, in this world of organization and nationalism, everyone must have some citizenship; so each tribe of Lapps has citizenship in the country where the tribe spends most of the year. For the people we have photographed, this country of citizenship is Sweden.

The Lapps are small, sturdy people—the women average less than five feet in height, the men just a bit more. They are not Scandinavian in racial background; apparently they belong neither to the Caucasoid stock nor to the Mongoloid. Where they came from no one knows with any exactness, nor when they established themselves in this northerly home. But through studying a trail of potsherds and other remains of human habitation leading westward along the coast of the Arctic Sea, anthropologists have decided that the Lapps probably came from the region of the distant Ural Mountains. Probably they came following, even in those far-off times, the herds of wild reindeer as the herds kept pace with the retreating ice of the last Glacial Age. They have been following the reindeer ever since.

For thousands of years, the Samer were simply hunters. With the help of spears, clubs and traps they wastefully slaughtered

Two Lapp herdsmen sup beside the fire at twilight in the Land of the Midnight Sun.

Spring finds the reindeer herds starting northward on their long journey.

Several families travel together with their herds on the long, hard trek.

Summer pasture lies far ahead of the reindeer on the high slopes of the mountains.

the big deer down through many centuries, and as has happened with peoples all over the globe, they slowly decided that it was not only more economical but easier to domesticate the animals. They divided them into herds and now travel in small groups of families, called "sitas," each following its own herd on the great migrations which mark the slow turn of the arctic year.

More and more of the people, in recent years, have become settled fishermen or even farmers. But some, like the families we shall follow, still set their calendars by the reindeer and follow their herds around the year.

ON THE TRAIL

The year of these people has eight seasons instead of four.

During spring, summer, autumn and winter, they live in fairly settled homes. But in between, in the periods known as spring-summer, summer-autumn, autumn-winter and winter-spring, they are on the move.

Winter-spring comes in mid-May. Then, though the land still lies deep in snow, we may see a herd of some fifteen hundred reindeer starting north for the summer in the high pastures. This is a combined herd of several families, each herd with its own special, registered "brand"—done by cropping the ears of the reindeer. The families, as well as the herds, travel together for mutual help on the long and difficult journey ahead. They make up a sita.

The land they must cover is a network of waterways, and the reindeer's traditional migratory routes tend to follow these water-trails. For the first part of the long trek north, frozen lakes and rivers serve as ice-paved highways, and over them the stream-lined, single-runnered sleds, called "akjas" or "pulkas," move smoothly along behind their reindeer steeds.

These sleds are examples of the ingenious simplicity of the Samer's craftsmanship. They are boatlike on their single runners—as slim and flexible and delicate of balance as canoes. And they are watertight, in case of emergency, though only about six inches deep for their six feet of length.

The driver wears his single rein wound around his forearm, so that if the light craft should be upset, he will be dragged along and will not lose the reindeer; for no halter is used. There is no bridle, and the beast is not held in by shafts. There is simply a single rawhide thong, which passes beneath his belly and between his hind legs, to connect him to the sled. This is perhaps wise, since reindeer are not really very tame. But it leaves the driver with full reponsibility for steering the craft with movements of his body, and for braking it on downhill grades.

MAKING CAMP

When the herd pauses, camp is made. While the deer search out the succulent mosses beneath the snow, and tender new lichen growth clinging to the rocks, down from the pack-reindeer's loads come the portable tents, called "katas." These tents, usually made of canvas, are quickly raised on their framework of poles, and a layer of brushwood is spread over their earthen floors.

Inside, across the doorway of the tent, a log is laid. A visitor may enter the tent uninvited, for finding shelter in the Arctic is often a matter of life or death. But he may not, without permission, cross this log into the heart of the home. Never should he step beyond the central fire; for the back of the tent, where food and supplies are kept, is an area sacred to the family. Nor may the guest, if invited to spend the night, sleep on the same side of the fire with the family. Space is reserved for him on the other side.

Provisions for the journey are safely stored on high platforms called "luovvos."

The herdsmen do not take the time to make camp when they stop for short meals.

Fresh-caught fish from the icy river make a delicious meal for the herdsmen.

Over this central fire, the food is cooked—perhaps fish fresh from a frozen stream, though more often it is dried or frozen reindeer meat. Soon after the evening meal, the fire is banked; the reindeerskin rolls which have served as seats are unrolled into beds, and soon the camp is quiet for the night. This stop will not be a long one, for the cows are anxious to move on.

The goal of the cows is the slope of Mt. Akka, their traditional calving spot. There the herdsmen set up spring quarters, for one of their seasonal stops. And soon, one by one, the wobbly-legged calves appear. Now the guard on the herd is tightened, for the great enemy of the reindeer is the arctic wolf, and new calves are naturally the most vulnerable prey of all.

As the weather turns warm, the herders build a platform of roughly assembled logs. On it they heap their heavy winter furs, to be picked up again as the sita passes this way on the southward trek before winter sets in. It is perfectly safe to leave them

A thick layer of turf makes a warm insulation on the summer shelter of the Lapp family.

there through the summer, for the Samer are an honest folk, who would not think of touching anyone else's property.

As soon as the new calves are ready to travel, on they move again to the high country. And here many of the sitas keep permanent huts in the spots to which they return year after year for their summer stay.

If there are not enough huts to go around for all the families in the group, it is no great problem to build another. Up goes a center pole, across goes a beam. Down from the beam slant other poles, and the framework is complete. Deft ax strokes strip pale bark from birch trees. Knowing hands blanket the sloping poles with the bark, then pack down the birchbark layer with thick blocks of sod fetched by the children, who eagerly join the work crew. And soon a new sod house is ready, well insulated against chill winds, without the use of a nail or a peg.

AROUND THE FIRE

Homemade bread is a staple of the Lapp diet.

This one-room house holds all the Lapp's treasures, for with him, the family is the core of life. Here are his children, often with an old, dependable dog trained to act as nursemaid for the baby, to free the mother for her many tasks. Here is his wife, loyal and dependable, busying herself with half a hundred activities—baking bread perhaps, or weaving bright, warm fabrics in age-old designs.

Perhaps his wife is preparing coffee for visitors. This is quite a ritual. First the coffee beans must be roasted in an iron kettle swung over the fire and stirred with a stick as they roast. Then out comes the old-fashioned coffee mill, and the fragrant beans are ground. Next, into the pot they go for boiling, and when the rich aroma tells that the coffee is done, into the pot goes a dried

In the Land of the Midnight Sun, bedtime often comes while the sun is shining.

Mealtime in the Lapp home is popular with the children, as it is everywhere.

Both men and women go fishing in Lapland's arctic lakes to lay in an ample supply.

Lapp girls and women work hard to gather the cloudberries ripening on the hills.

The long days of the arctic summer are a good time for cleaning the harvest of fish.

fish—scales and all—to settle the grounds, so the brew will be amber-clear. A few coarse salt crystals, and it is ready for pouring into small, dipper-shaped white birch cups, beautifully decorated with primitive designs. The cups are washed both before and after use.

The coffee is passed around on a long, narrow tray decorated like the cups, and with it comes a long, bread-like loaf of sugar, with a special pair of pincers to break off a bit for each drinker. The Samer custom is to place the sugar lump in your mouth and drink the coffee through it, inhaling with a cheerful sucking sound. There is no cream, but you can have goat's milk instead.

The good wife has homemade goat's-milk cheese on hand, too, well aged and pungent. Sometimes she puts a piece of cheese into a cup, adds hot water, and makes it into a drink.

THE MIDNIGHT SUN

The days lengthen until dawn overtakes sundown. For a few weeks the sun circles the wide horizon, never sinking from sight. The brief, dazzling summer is at hand, with its spangling of flowers, tart lingonberries ripening on the hills, and fish jumping in the crystal waters.

Now it is really difficult for the children to go to bed by day; but the grownups are glad of the light, for summer is short, and there is much to do. This is the time to lay in a supply of fish from the arctic lakes, so the women venture out in their boats with nets and barrels for the catch. The men may go fishing too, and they hunt, as well, for the small fur-bearing creatures of the north, whose pelts they can sell in town.

More of their tasks, though, have to do with the reindeer, for reindeer are their staff of life, supplying not only the necessary food and clothing but material for barter in the winter markets in town.

FROM REINDEER SKINS

Skins from recently butchered animals must be stretched and dried. The meat itself does not demand much care in this climate; it need only be hung out of reach of the herd dogs, for it will not spoil readily.

As for the skins, they must be cured, scraped to softness, perhaps laid for a time in the bed of an icy stream. When they are ready, they will be fashioned into blankets, rugs, clothing and rawhide boots.

So important are these sturdy, comfortable boots to a people constantly on the move that in greeting one another Laplanders ask, "How are your feet?"

New boots are constantly in the making, the seams stitched with reindeer sinew thread. The Lapland wife makes the thread herself. She separates the tendons into slender strands, rolls these against her cheek, then draws them out between her teeth into a smooth cord. This sinew thread waterproofs the seams.

To seal the loose-fitting boot tops, leggings are woven on a hand loom of ancient design.

The women of Lapland make boots of "bellingar," the skin from the reindeers' legs.

Reindeer skin must be treated by "grazing" before it can be sewed into boots.

With these leggings tightly wrapped about his calves, the herdsman will be well prepared for wind or water. He wears no socks, but instead stuffs his boots with fresh sedge grass, which he has come to call "shoe hay."

Trousers, coats and dresses are made of reindeer skins, too, worn hairside in for extra warmth, skinside in when the weather is milder. But for Sunday best, bright, handwoven fabrics have a place all their own.

Boot laces are made from reindeer skin; the thread for stitching the seams from tendons.

The Lapps have a deep sense of reverence and greatly enjoy their church services.

As summer draws to a close, migration is again in the minds of the Laplanders.

SUNDAY MEETING

The Samer's heritage is the glory of the earth. He tells time by the stars, weather by a glance at the sky. He does not ask a life of ease; in his simple existence in this harsh land he finds many blessings for which he is inspired to give thanks. So, moved by a reverence for things of the spirit, and with a deep sense of gratitude, he has built temples in the wilderness.

Some hundreds of years ago the sun, the thunder and the wind were the Lapp's tribal gods. Each spot of earth he trod had, he believed, its own guardian spirit, and his priests in drum-inspired raptures told him the way to appease these gods, that he might have health for his family and a safe journey with his herd of reindeer.

About two hundred years back, missionaries came to tell the Lapps about the Christian church and faith. The whole people (there are about 35,000 Lapps today) were converted, and now they are devout Christians, gathering whenever they can for Sunday devotions.

Schools, too, have caught up with the wanderers. The Swedish government sends teachers to move with the sitas on their mi-

grations. School is conducted in a special kata, a tent set aside for this purpose. Because the tent is rather low and cramped, with sides sloping to the ground, the children do not rise to their feet to recite, but instead kneel. They are taught the Swedish language, numbers, local geography, and natural history based on the plants and animals of their wide countryside. And they are taught good living habits suited to their way of life.

The Lapps, who have been Christians for two hundred years, have churches like this one.

THE SMELL OF WINTER

Arctic summer is but a moment of fleeting loveliness. The wild flowers soon wither, the wind turns chill. The first snowfall brings the smell of winter, and the deer begin to stir.

The stirring of the deer is the signal for the families to move, too, heading south to beat the fast-approaching cold; for neither deer nor man is capable of withstanding the winter here.

Back down the rough slopes they retrace their steps, both herds and families of the sita. Down pours the river of tossing horns, down to the waterways. But this time they find no smooth, icy highways fit for hoof and sled. The lakes and rivers are still open, blocking the path of the herd.

For the families this is fine; they can travel many miles of the return journey by boat. And many today have boats fitted with sturdy outboard motors. Still, leave-taking is a wistful time. For some of the honored old people this may be the last backward glance at scenes filled with a lifetime of memories.

Now the noonday sun hugs the horizon, and the autumn gold with which it paints the clouds is reflected in the sea. This strange, wild beauty warns of winter and of storms to come. The wise Lapps heed the warning; they waste few moments in backward glances. Heaping their boats with people and goats, they are off, with a roar of the outboards, stirring up behind them, in the quiet waters, wakes of molten gold.

AUTUMN ROUNDUP

For the reindeer, the trip south is rugged. Instead of walking on a smooth-surfaced highway of snow-covered ice, they are forced to cross icy rivers by swimming, an activity for which most reindeer do not particularly care.

Summer pasture on the Akka Mountain is left behind as the cold winter approaches.

The family starts its fall migration by boat, since the rivers are still free from ice.

In the autumn, the herds are rounded up in big corrals for the annual sorting.

Once settled in their winter quarters, the Lapps have time to visit the markets.

Reindeer racing, with teams pulling light sleds, is a feature of the winter holiday.

Friends and relatives join the bridal couple in the march to the altar to say their vows.

If one lead deer can be lured into the water, the herd will quickly follow. But this is a precarious time, for the slightest distraction—a sudden movement or strange noise—may panic the herd there on the shore.

A rope is tied around the head of the lead deer, known as a "judas." He is pulled down the bank and out into deep water. All is tensely silent but for the chug of the motor and the frantic splashing of the "judas." But instinct conquers fear, and the deer starts to swim for his life behind the boat, following it out into midstream. And the men aboard relax a bit as they see the herd pouring down into the water, following the leader as planned.

The crossing is accomplished without incident. After a shiver and a shake on the far shore, the herd is ready to move on. And there is no time to lose. Already a thin snow is swirling down from the Arctic, harbinger of much, much more to come. Herdsmen and herd dogs urge the animals forward. Instinct, too, pushes the deer on in their ten-thousand-year-old pattern.

Down they come, out of the hills into the flatter lowlands with their woods of birch and pine. And safely once again they reach the southern corrals.

Here the reindeer, unaccustomed to confinement, wheel anxiously about inside the big stockade. Fawns search frantically for their mothers; young bucks stamp and toss their heads in bewilderment. And soon the confusion is increased as lassos whirl in the air and drop over antlers.

This is the "rarkning," the time of separating the individual herds, which takes place twice a year. Each owner recognizes his own ear-notch on his personal stock. And though he works afoot, instead of mounted, he rarely misses with his lasso.

The sorting of the herd accomplishes more than the identification of stock by owners; animals are sorted for breeding and beef as well. Some of the choice stock are marked with a slap of paint, to be led off for butchering. Unmarked strays are sold and the money is used for the aged. Others are chosen for breeding, in an effort to upgrade the herd.

Though the lassoed deer may balk, and the herd mill about, here in the corral the men are clearly in command. And beneath the hub-bub, an orderly routine flows along.

WINTER HOLIDAY

Once the rarkning is over, the Lapps move on to settled winter quarters, and vacation time comes.

This is the time to visit the cities, with their great market places. For in these markets the Lapps' handiwork of the summer will be offered for sale. And here they can see, to marvel at or to buy, the strange and varied goods of the outside world.

This is the place to see other Lapps. The tribes recognize each other by the special designs of the women's shawls and lace-frilled bonnets and the men's bright caps.

There is weaving for sale at the stands; there are fur pelts, cured hides and blankets and pants, there are boots and scarves.

But for the men there is a more rugged sport than wandering among market stalls. This truly Lapp sport is reindeer racing, with teams hitched to swift, light sleds.

Winter is the time for weddings, too. All over Lapland the bells ring out as friends and relatives join bridal parties and march in line to the church. The groom, with his bride beside him, travels in the center.

To the Samer, a wedding is much more than a simple ceremony. It is a promise for the future, the start of a new family to carry the proud nomad tradition into the coming years.

The newly married couple stands together on the threshold of a new life. With devotion to each other, and with a heritage of courage behind them, they wait for the turning seasons to sound the call of the high mountains again. Once more, as the great herds answer that call, the People of the Reindeer will answer it too. And the trek will start once more.

A people who spend so much time in near-solitude enjoy their winter gatherings.

THE HIGHLANDS

Scotland's Crown

THE village street has a stern, plain air. Above, the cloud-massed skies are gray. The stones of the worn old pavements underfoot glisten from the recent drip of rain. But now down the street comes a marching man, over his shoulder a bagpipe. The cold, misty air fairly shimmers with sound, with the mournful, monotonous beat of the bass and over it swirling the melody's skirl. All by himself the man is a parade that causes every watcher's heart to leap. Overhead, the very clouds themselves seem split by the sound, for gold sunlight pours down in one of the Highlands' "bright intervals."

BAGPIPES AND TARTANS

The wheeze and wail of the bagpipe is the music most dear to the Highlander's ear. In the old days, every self-respecting village, every chieftain of a clan maintained full-time pipers. No festival, funeral, wedding or battle charge was complete without them. And the strange music lightened the workers' labors and the loneliness of herdsmen in the hills.

The instrument did not originate in Scotland. It came there with the early Scots when they migrated from Ireland. But its ancestry goes back six thousand years to ancient Chaldea. Starting with simple shepherds' pipes, some ancient genius added an airtight leather bag as a reservoir for wind and produced a link between the pipes of Pan and a primitive organ. The bagpipe, in fact, was often used in Irish church music, before the day of the organ, to sustain with its droning fixed bass note the key note of religious chants.

But it was in the Highlands that the bagpipe found its true home. Even today you may meet a piper on any village street, and hear his lively music at any Highland wedding. Here and there in a small shop attached to a village house you will find an old craftsman at work with his apprentice,

making pipes to order in the old-fashioned way.

Piping is still taught at Edinburgh Castle to pipe-majors of all Highland regiments. For many a battle has been turned by the courageous forward march of pipers when common sense dictated retreat.

About the tartans—

When the early Scots came from Ireland, they all dressed in much the same way. But because each clan had a pride that ran fierce and high—and perhaps also to make it easy to tell friend from foe—it took to wearing its own plaid, known as a tartan and revered with fierce loyalty even today.

First there is the kilt—the short, pleated skirt so well suited to a climb over rough ground. With it today is worn a jacket. And the small blanket once worn as a sort of cloak has become the "plaid," a scarf worn draped over the left shoulder on special occasions. Since the kilt has no pockets, a pouch called a sporran is worn suspended from a cord about the waist. And a bonnet or a tam-o'-shanter cap jauntily tops it all.

Who are the people who cling with pride to this colorful old way of dress? They are

No Highland wedding is truly complete without a piper to pipe the tunes.

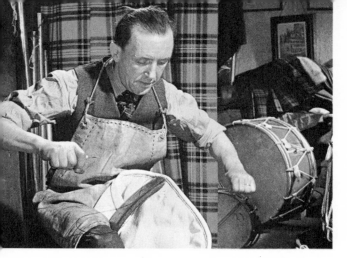

The craft of the bagpipe maker remains unchanged; here he sews up sheepskin bags.

A potential customer tries out his "blow" on a set of pipes in the bagpipe shop.

In the reign of the Emperor Hadrian, this wall was built to shut out the troublesome Picts.

the rugged Highland Scots, the people of our tale. Scotland glories, to be sure, in her contributions to Western culture. Mother of great universities and museums, libraries and medical schools, she is also famed for industry and commerce; and majestic ocean liners launched from ultra-modern shipyards carry her renown across the seven seas. But while the Scotsmen are proud of this modern culture, they take an equal and more personal pride in their historic tradition.

Tradition is based upon a fiery independence of spirit which stands even between the Highlander and the Lowlander of the fertile eastern Scottish plains. And it is the Highlander, pursuing his rugged way of life in his cold, damp, rocky land, who most ardently keeps the Scottish traditions alive.

PICTS AND ROMANS

As much as two thousand years ago, when the Roman legions of Julius Caesar began their conquest of the great isle of Britain, the people of the northern highlands already had a name and a fame all their own. Picts, meaning "painted," was the name by which they were called; and their fame was for a fierceness and warlike nature disproportionate to their small and wiry frames. Their rude dwellings were underground, and, since they often ventured out bent upon mischief, stories of brownies and elves grew up, which still haunt the Highland countryside.

The Romans gave up trying to tame the Picts. In fact, during the reign of the Emperor Hadrian, they built a massive wall across the countryside from firth to sea, to keep out the troublesome tribes. Parts of Hadrian's Wall remain today, a monument to the independence of ancient Highlanders.

The Picts were probably glad enough to stay in their Highlands. But they were not left to themselves. Celts drifted north from

Britain; Scots from Ireland landed on the west coast and the western isles; Norsemen raided coast and islands and sometimes even stayed to rule. There was continual fighting during the next thousand years, for the Norse and the Scots were wild warriors worthy of their fierce Pict opponents.

Even after long, bloody centuries had blended the warring tribes into one people, the fighting went on—clan against Highland clan. Many of the Highlanders' most rousing tales are of the clan feuds and massacres; many of their most revered monuments are scenes of these battles or heroes' graves.

But life in the Highlands today has little of fighting or marching to music. It is often lonely for the crofter, in his cottage or out on the cold, misty moors with his sheep. He probably has a few cattle, too, out on the pasture land. For the rugged Highland cattle, in their shaggy double coats, though they are very slow growing and not the best for beef, have a usefulness all the same. They eat the coarse grasses, while the sheep crop the sweeter and finer ones. This keeps a bal-

ance in the pasture. When, years ago, most farmers turned to woolgrowing and let the cattle go, they soon found the coarse grasses and bracken taking over their grazing lands. So they brought the cattle back.

It is the wool coats of the Highland sheep which provide a living for most Highlanders. And perhaps the best place to trace the industry from sheep's back to man's back is on the islands of the Inner and Outer Hebrides. They are really a part of the Highlands, and the loneliest part of all—or so it might seem to an outsider viewing these beautiful but desolate scraps of land flung out across a stormy sea.

The Western Islands are not merely part of the Highlands geologically; they also share the Celtic heritage and, thanks to their isolation, preserve it quite unchanged. Their only contact with the outside world is maintained by means of the chugging little one-cylinder-engined boats called "puffers."

News of a "puffer's" arrival sends the farmer to harnessing up his rig.

The flat-bottomed puffer runs in with the tide on a flat Scottish beach.

PUFFER AGROUND

As there are few ports in the Hebrides, and none at all on some of the small, rocky islands, the puffer simply looks for a rock-free beach and runs in with the tide. Being flat-bottomed, it stays serenely upright as the

The crew of the puffer unloads the goods they have brought into the farmer's cart.

tide retreats. And there is plenty of time for leisurely business before the next high tide.

The farmer has time to hitch up his cart and let the horse make his ambling way out across the broad, smooth stretch of shining sand that is the beach at low tide. And the genial crew can take their time at unloading into his cart. The crew may have only the one order to deliver at this port of call. The twelve-hour wait before the next high tide gives them ample time for exchanging news and views of the day, and perhaps for a good dinner ashore.

In many of the islands' cottages, most of the family income results from the women's work. The men trade a few cattle or watch the sheep on the hills. Many of them still go fishing, although that industry has dwindled in recent years. But the main industry of the islanders is the making of the famous Harris Tweed. They have even set up an association, which says with honest pride: "Harris Tweed means a tweed made from pure virgin wool produced in Scotland, spun, dyed and finished in the Outer Hebrides and hand-woven by the islanders at their own homes in the islands of Lewis, Harris, Ulst, Barrs and their several purtenances and all known as the Outer Hebrides."

HARRIS TWEED

Harris is not really an island itself, but properly the southern half of a long island named Lewis & Harris. This two-county island is often called Long Island for simplicity. But the name Long Island is also used to refer to the whole chain of islands of the Outer Hebrides.

Even the name "tweed" is based on an error. About a century and a half ago, a Scottish manufacturer sent to a London merchant a shipment of twill. Now the Scottish name for twill is "tweel." And in those days before the typewriter, when all business correspondence was carried on in long-hand, it was easy enough to mistake a letter. So a London clerk misread the word as "tweed." Since this is the name of a well-known Scottish river, it seemed sensible enough to him and to many others. The cloth was put on the market as "tweed." And often it is capitalized, as if it were named for the river.

Wherever the name may have come from, the fame of Harris Tweed has spread afar. Some authorities claim that the arts of spinning and weaving originated with the Celts. And certainly some of the world's most expert handweaving of today is being done in a tiny area in Scotland where Celtic culture is still dominant.

The lichen called "crottal" is scraped from the rocks for use in dying wool for tweed.

So highly is Harris Tweed valued that the supply cannot keep up with the demand. But the demand can wait. The proud people of the islands will not change the way in which their tweed is made. It is still produced, as it always has been, in the scattered crofters' homes. The women, with few exceptions, do the weaving. And they use the same kind of equipment they used in the days when they spun and wove for their families alone.

In the early days, native sheep provided

Natural dyes are stewed into a thin brew, into which the wool is dipped.

The spinning of true Harris Tweed is a cottage craft; most of the work is done by women.

all the wool; but now that the industry has grown, the rocky hillsides cannot support the number of sheep whose fleeces are needed; nor are there men enough on the islands to care for them. So wool, already cleaned and carded, is brought in from the mainland by puffer. The majority of the women do their own spinning on their gently creaking old wheels. Some few do buy wool already spun; but the proud words "hand-spun" are missing from the trademark stamped on their finished tweed.

Before weaving, of course, the wool must be dyed. And the dyes are as local and traditional as the wheels and looms. You'll find no range of synthetic colors in true Harris Tweeds; purest vegetable dyes are used, mostly in warm browns and blues. Most famous of the local dyes is crottal, source of the reddish browns. It is made from a lichen scraped from rocks and stewed out-of-doors over a fire fragrant with driftwood or peat. Blues are obtained by stewing elderberries or blackberries with alum; other roots, lichens and leaves are also used, stewed in a watery brew. The wool is dipped into the dye until the color penetrates to the depth of shade desired. Then the wool is whisked out, washed again and dried.

Next the warp threads are strung up on the loom, and deft fingers and feet work in pattern together, flicking the shuttle across with the weft, and beating the threads firm.

When the tweed leaves the loom it is rough and hard. To soften the fibers and plump them up to give the finished cloth a close web, a finishing process called "waulking" is used. "Waulk" is Scottish for "walk," and in early times this softening was done with the feet. Indeed, in some lands it still is. But in Scotland today it is customarily done by machines.

Only occasionally is the traditional method still used. Then the newly woven tweed is soaked in soapy water and laid loosely on a long table. Several women seated around the table "tumble" the cloth, moving it from hand to hand and kneading it as though it were dough. To give their movements rhythm—and to brighten and lighten the work—they sing a traditional waulking song, the sweet lilt of high-pitched Gaelic voices filling the small, dim room.

Its texture softened by waulking, the tweed will shrink, gaining firmness, as it dries. While it is still damp, it will be wound tightly around a narrow board called a core. This will keep the weft straight and prevent too much shrinkage. And now the tweed is ready for shipping, and for sale in the four corners of the British Commonwealth and beyond.

As it comes off the loom, the tweed fabric is rough and hard to the touch.

The women work together around a table to soften, or "waulk," the newly woven tweed.

A Highland fling, danced to the mouth music of the guests, is a fine sight to see.

THE CEILIDH

When the creak of the spinning wheel falls silent in the evening, or the shuttle on the loom lies still, there may be a "ceilidh"— "kay´ lee," it might sound to an English-accustomed ear. This is a truly Gaelic gathering, and a chief recreation on the western isles and in the Highlands generally. In many a remote village, one house is known as the "ceilidh house." It is the place where people gather in the evening, hoping for a visit or a bit of fun. What better way could there be to celebrate a birthday or other anniversary, than with an evening of mouth music at the ceilidh house?

Mouth music, of course, is singing, the greatest Gaelic joy. There is a treasure of fine old Gaelic songs, and each villager knows many of them. Now and again there will be a solo, with the group joining in on the choruses. And to lubricate the vocal chords, there will of course be refreshments —tea for the women, and good Scotch whisky brought by the puffer for the men.

There may be dancing, too—solo Highland flings, or two or four couples joining in a reel. But always there is some food on hand —whatever the guests might wish—and always there is good singing, and good feeling, at a Highland family "bust."

HALLOWEEN

For the young, perhaps the jolliest of celebrations comes on the eve of Allhallows, or All Saints' Day. For Halloween falls upon the eve of the Druid New Year. And many old traditions of the Picts and the Scots, from the days before their conversion to Christianity, come from the religion of the Druids with their sacred groves.

The Druids worshiped nature, and especially the sun. Since the sun was considered a power for good, the powers of evil were thought to be at their strongest during the long nights of winter. So when darkness fell on the last day of their year—our October 31 —the Druid priests lighted huge bonfires on hilltops and offered sacrifices.

The "Druid priest" casts his magical spell over the annual Halloween celebration.

Granite for curling stones is drilled and blasted from the craggy walls of the quarry.

The roughly shaped blocks are stacked for shipping to the factory on the mainland.

The object of these ceremonies was protection from the power of evil; and when the fires burned down, torches were lighted from the sacred flames to carry the protection abroad. These torches were the forerunners of Halloween lanterns, carved with hideous faces to frighten away the evil spirits. Today the children's lanterns are often carved from hollowed-out turnips, which are as plentiful at this season in the Highlands as pumpkins are in the United States.

Dry leaves are used as decorations, because this is the season of decay in the earth. Best of all are twigs of the hazel tree, "the magic tree that wizards love," from which their wands were made.

On this night, as the old year approaches its death, legend says that the veil between the worlds of humans and of spirits grows very thin. Spirits walk the earth: the kindly ones of the dead come back to visit their homes; the mischievous ones of fairies and elves scamper about on their pranks; and fearsome witches gather for secret meetings in lonely spots—especially graveyards.

Those with "the sight" on this night of nights can glimpse the future and spell it out, following the clues of egg whites dribbled into water; of a finger poked into a bowl while the "seer" is blindfolded; and of charms full of meaning hidden in food.

Master of the revels is a man dressed as a Druid priest clad in a long white robe, wreathed with the oak leaf crown for wisdom. With his hazel wand he directs the games—ducking for apples, reels and the rest. Every wave of his magic wand must circle sunwise, the Druid way, never "widdershins," the witches' way, which is unlucky. And the marching and dancing of the gaily costumed group must all turn in the proper sunwise way. Thus, under the guidance of respected old traditions, another Highland year is ushered in with all due ceremony.

CURLING

In the summer there is golfing in the Highlands; but in winter the great outdoor sport is curling.

This is a game for the stout and hardy. For the requirements include a snell (sharp) wind, black ice, thick clothes and a good hot toddy or a flask of Scotch. When the ice is a firm five inches thick, it's time for a bonspiel (great match). Then the smooth, round forty-five pound stones go spinning across the glass-smooth loch, or pond. And if a skim of water should lie upon the ice, threatening to slow down the ball, out will come a player with a small broom, sooping (sweeping) the water off the ice.

The curling stones themselves are a pretty sight, smoothly curved from blocks of granite, with handles set in. And the manufacture of these stones is a typically Scottish industry. Much of the granite comes from Aisla Craig, a small high island in the Firth of Clyde, which is itself shaped something like a curling stone. The island is an almost solid chunk of granite and from its steep cliffs slabs are drilled and blasted away, which are then chipped roughly into blocks somewhat larger than the finished stones.

In the mainland factory, the rough blocks are turned by hard steel revolving cutters. Then they are ground down, with fine accuracy, against carborundum bricks. During the grinding and polishing—which involves more carborundum bricks and secret abrasives—water is used as a lubricant and cooler, to prevent friction-heated rocks from splitting. The center section, called the striking hand,

In a curling match, the skim of water is swept away so as not to slow down the stone.

The sharp, cold Highland winter is the time for the great curling matches.

where the stones hit together during play, is roughened to provide a sort of cushioning against splitting in the game.

The handle, sometimes embellished with fancy touches, is screwed to a bolt which passes through the stone. After long use has worn or chipped the bottom of the stone, the handle can simply be reversed, and the stone used upside down. For the Scotsman makes the most of what he has, and never lets anything go to waste.

At twilight the herring fishermen turn their boats towards the shore.

THE HERRING

This philosophy applies of course to work as well as to play; and the main business of life for many a Scot, passed down as a heritage from long generations of seafaring ancestors, is herring fishing. In an old chronicle dated 709, herring fishing is mentioned as an established industry.

The shoals (schools) of herring appear off different Scottish coasts at different seasons of the year; so the fishing can be almost a year-round occupation, although summer is the busiest time.

Through the long, cloud-heavy summer dusk, the diesel-powered herring-drifter makes its way across choppy seas to the fishing grounds. Milky water is a sign that the goal is near; that and the circling of gulls above. For it is plankton, the tiny, swarming animal life which herring feast upon, that turn the water white as milk. And the gulls, in turn, are there to feast upon the herring as they rise by night to feed on the plankton just beneath the surface of the sea.

The herring themselves are not easy to spot; for once they attain their growth, their coloring protects them well. Large hunting fish looking up from below see only a blur of silvery white, in which pale fish bellies smoothly merge with pale light filtering down from the sky. To the fisherman's eye the blue-green backs blend just as smoothly with the mottled blue-green tones of the sea. But the gulls, wheeling hungrily above, see the massing of shoals in tight formation below the surface, and they scream the news.

Now it is time to shoot the nets. The skipper and his eight-man crew are all at attention, and the speed of the motor is cut. When just the spot they have chosen is reached, over the side to windward goes the "fleet"—the long curtain of nets strung together on a rope to form a wall of mesh perhaps a mile and a half long. A fleet this long takes close to sixty fifty-yard nets, held close to the surface by airtight canvas floats called buffs.

Now the engine is shut off. The vessel drifts with the tide; and from this comes its name of "drifter." Behind it bobs the long line of white buffs, marking the waiting fleet.

Through the gray night the cold sea winds buffet the long, low boat and its crew, flinging icy spray up over the men straining to watch those buffs. Now and again a man may try to snatch forty winks of sleep; for the hardest time is still to come. But it pays to keep a keen eye on the weather, lest the thirty- to fifty-mile distance to shore prove too much in a wild night of storm. And it pays to keep a wise eye on the nets, for they can be broken by a great rush of fish.

The skipper calls for a test net to be pulled in; and his eyes brighten under their tufted brows at the mass of tossing, squirming silver in the taut-pulled net. When he gives the signal for pulling in the fleet, the real work begins. On the slippery-wet and rolling deck, the men brace themselves for the long pull. Ropes are sodden; nets weighed down with struggling fish are clumsy to handle at best.

Hour after hour the men toil on. Three hours may see the catch aboard in smooth summer seas, but nine hours is common, and during a storm, with a wild wind slashing at men and nets and fish, it may take twelve to fourteen hours to pull in the fleet.

It's a thrilling time when the silver hoard pours over the side in a living tide. Now the hatch cover on the deck is tugged back, and the mass of herring slides into the hold, filling the waiting lockers. The lockers are compartmented to avoid a pile-up of fish that might crush those on the bottom.

On and on pours the silver tide, as net after net is raised. A good many of the fish fall splashing back into the sea; but chances are another section of the fleet is waiting to capture them, or they fall into a special bag-net attached to the drifter's gunwale.

The last net comes up. The haul is in. The motor leaps to life with a roar. Now comes the homeward race through choppy seas, and the danger is far from past. Every man feels the strain of the pull for port; for these men of the crew are no mere hirelings. They are "joint adventurers" sharing the proceeds of the haul; so the strain of the skipper is their strain, until the catch is landed and sold.

Time is a factor in more ways than one. It is summer, and the herring are fatter than in other seasons, hence more quick, without ice, to spoil; and the freshest bring the highest price. There is an old tradition, too, that the first boat in gets a specially high price. So the diesel engines strain, with the drifters wallowing in almost awash from the weight of the fish in their holds. Storm clouds now hold a terrible threat, for even a stalled engine is enough to swamp a heavy-laden boat. But slowly the welcoming roofs of the harbor town, glinting in a watery light, rise up from the seas ahead; and a load lifts from the hearts of the men.

This lovely Highland village, standing beside its loch, is a center for the herring fisheries.

THE DANUBE

River Highway of Central Europe

HIGH in the beautiful Black Forest of Germany, three small streams unite to form the Danube, Europe's most important river highway. The only major European river flowing west to east, for 1,750 miles it travels across the heart of Central Europe, gathering its waters from more than 300 tributaries which rise in many different countries. Far to the east it flows out at last into the Black Sea, building there a delta composed of soil borne from all the lands of Central Europe in its 300,000 square-mile basin.

IN TIMES LONG PAST

For well over two thousand years the Danube has been important in European history. As long ago as the time of the fabled Trojan War, the rich early civilizations of the eastern Mediterranean reached northern Europe and even Britain via the Danube, and continued to for many centuries. During the proudest centuries of the Roman Empire, the long, shining curves of the Danube marked the frontier of the empire. Beyond lay the realm of the untamed Teutonic tribes. Bits of a 150-mile-long string of fortifications, of the walls of the Emperor Trajan, of border outposts and settlements, of the famous stone-paved imperial roads of Rome and even the ruins of great theaters still brood drowsily over countryside which has long since forgotten the sound of the Roman legion's boots under the heavier tramp of other armies which have marched and fought across this valley.

For the valley of the Danube, leading as it does into the heart of Europe, has been a favorite route for invaders from the East. The Huns from the steppes of central Asia, riding their small, swift ponies, raced far up the Danube in late Roman times, looting and pillaging. In the centuries that followed, great droughts in Asia forced many tribes to migrate toward the west. The Avars, the Slavs, the Magyars and finally the Turks stormed up the valley, settling in as conquerors. The Turks, emboldened by their conquest of Constantinople, reached the very gates of Vienna in 1683 before they were stopped; and they held some areas along the Danube for 500 years.

From the opposite direction, from the West, came the Franks under Charlemagne, the Bavarians, hordes of hungry Crusaders en route by land to the Holy Wars, and, much later, the armies of Napoleon and those of the German Reich.

During the Middle Ages, feudal lords built a chain of fortresses along the river to stem the tides of invasion. These sturdy structures,

The Danube rises in the Alpine lake region of southern Germany.

Young people in hay carts creak down the shady roads for a picnic in the Black Forest.

now in ruins, with swallows nesting in their grass-grown walls, still loom high above the river. To eastern Austria they give the name of "Land of Castles," and many towns still recall their days of grandeur with historical pageants held in castle courtyards. One, the keep of Lockenhaus, has stood proudly for 750 years, guarding its stretch of the river.

Even today, all is not peaceful along the Danube. The bitter dissension among Danubian peoples during the two World Wars and their interim has not all been healed. The Russians have not long since left Vienna —their departure giving rise to a burst of activity in building, industry and the arts similar to that which followed release from the threat of the Turks. Even today, plowed

The Forest provides innumerable spots for the enjoyment of a lavish picnic lunch.

border strips mark the boundaries between Austria and Hungary and Czechoslovakia; and in dipping down into Yugoslavia and crossing into Romania and Bulgaria the mighty river, ignoring all national boundaries and political differences, flows through troubled lands.

But let us go back to the Alpine lake region of southern Germany where the river rises, and follow its course to the sea.

THE BLACK FOREST

In the hilly beauty of the Black Forest are found the Alpine pools of indigo hue from which, legend says, comes the color that gives the Danube its fame as the "beautiful blue Danube." Many less romantic souls claim that the Danube appears blue only to those in love. But even this is not too limiting, for this area has long been famed for romance. The ageless cliffs of the Alpine lakes have long echoed promises of love and eternal devotion between young men and women.

The Black Forest today is once again a happy land of picnic parties and laughter and song. There are fishermen in the brawling streams and peaceful hay carts creaking down the roads. There is sport on the rapids of the river for enthusiasts in their rubberized, water-tight canoes. And above the river the close-crowding hills make a richly beautiful rural scene, with toy picture-book villages nestling on the slopes, tall church spires beckoning over the woods, and beautiful castles crowning the rugged heights.

So the slim young river races, 2,000 feet above the sea, from Donaueschingen past Tuttlingen and Sigmaringen and on down to Ulm. Here it mirrors one of the tallest church steeples in the world, perhaps the very tallest. And here for the first time the river is wide enough and calm enough to be really navigable.

Young couples row on the smoothly flowing river beneath this romantic Hohenzollern castle near Sigmaringen.

Ulm makes the most of its river; its young people enjoy aquatic gymnastics, and everyone enjoys the annual water festival with its procession of floats—really afloat—lampooning everything in sight.

THROUGH BAVARIA

Life along the Danube is not all fun and games. There is industry and commerce as well on the river, though not as much as there might be because of all the frontiers to be crossed. Still, shiploads of coal and wheat have long traveled this water highway, and farther down, loads of petroleum. There are many short-run passenger steamers, and there is fishing enough to make quite an industry.

Regensburg, in eastern Bavaria, has been an important shipping terminal. It still prides itself on an out-of-door fish market where the fish are so fresh they are not always ready to admit that they have been caught. But more important, Regensburg provides a glimpse of a cross-section of history, cutting back through many centuries of time.

The wandering clock vendor travels about with his wares today just as his ancestors did.

Above Regensburg for more than 500 years stood the chief outpost of the Roman Empire's northern frontier. Charlemagne, a few centuries later, made his headquarters here on his eastward thrust. Another few hundred years after that, Regensburg was a meeting place for Crusaders starting for Jerusalem by the overland route. And in those days boatmen from Regensburg traveled down river to the Black Sea, then around to proud, weary old Constantinople, coming home full of wealth and worldly wisdom to build themselves great mansions which still stand along the river banks.

Up from the banks on the northern side the gentle, rounded slopes of the Bavarian forest rise to hazy mountains back in the distance. And as we float downstream, the mountains gradually close in upon the river. But here a side trip up a tributary, the Isar, beckons us to the town of Landshut.

The town of Landshut is the setting for a romantic traditional ceremony.

THE POLISH PRINCESS OF LANDSHUT

Nowhere are historical traditions carried on more elaborately than in this river town. Rich in old-world charm, Landshut looks much the same today as it did five centuries ago. And local citizens take great pride in reliving a page from their past.

In the self-same city hall which is in use today, the councilmen of Landshut met in 1475 to discuss the wisdom of accepting a Polish princess as the bride of their local duke. In traditional costumes they gather there today, sit about the council table and

The modern "Duke" greets his beautiful "Princess" in her ancient golden coach.

solemnly renew the ancient argument. After heated discussion, it is eventually agreed that they should welcome the Polish party. So the "groom," young Duke Georg, is cheered by crowds of his loyal "subjects" as he rides forth to his first meeting with the "Princess," chosen for the occasion from among the prettiest of the local girls.

Every detail is kept as authentic as possible, and the Princess arrives in the very same golden coach in which the beautiful Hedwig rode down from Poland in 1475. Vagabonds and camp followers straggle along behind, just as they did on that historic day so long ago. And the royal wedding is announced with a blare of trumpets.

Following the royal wedding, the real-life, long-ago groom took his bride to his ancestral home, Traunitz Castle, a landmark that still stands today. Here the bridal ball and ballet are reenacted in commemoration of the most lavish social event in all Europe during the fifteenth century.

THE CHILDREN'S VICTORY

In Dinkelsbühl, too, north of the river, an episode from the town's troubled past is commemorated today. The remains of a moat and fortified walls bear testimony to the town's existence through another era torn with strife. This was the Thirty Years' War, when conquering Swedish armies camped outside the city's gate to lay siege to Dinkelsbühl. The Swedish commander, the townsfolk well knew, had made up his mind to pillage the town once victory was in his hands.

After an heroic defense, the town was forced to surrender. And it was then that there occurred an unforgettable event. In through the gates of the city marched the conqueror, only to be met by a band of children. The children had come not to fight but to beg for mercy. And it so happened that in the front rank marched a boy with a face like that of the young son the Swedish commander had recently lost. Out of compassion born of his own grief, the conqueror relented and spared the city.

Each year, tribute is paid to these brave children of long ago, the rejoicing climaxed by the music of the Dinkelsbühl Boys' Band.

TIME OF DRAGONS

In contrast to pageants based on fact is one which is rooted in legend and lore of the Bohemian Forest—as meaningful to the people of the area as history could ever be. In the olden times the dark forests were inhabited, so the fears of the people told them, by fearsome, fire-breathing, man-devouring dragons; and one of these horrible dragons is still to be seen in Danubian pageantry.

Out from the forest ponderously waddles a yellow dragon, symbol of the fears and superstitions which beset the people of medieval times. Across the meadow he moves, snorting flame, and approaches the town gate of Furth-im-Wald. Now it happens that (at the time the pageant re-creates) the fighting menfolk of the city have all been called away to war. No match for a dragon, the women and children are helpless and defenseless.

The children of Dinkelsbühl saved their town from the Swedish invaders long ago.

Breathing clouds of smoke and looking quite terrifying, the fierce dragon enters the city.

Just when all hope seems at an end for the women and children, up rides the town's most gallant soldier, come home from the war. The people seem assured of deliverance, until someone has an unhappy thought. This most gallant warrior is, unfortunately, a commoner, and the slaying of dragons is a sport reserved to knighthood.

In a flash of genius, someone in the crowd takes a sword and promptly dubs the soldier "The White Knight."

Now, possessing at last a rank suitable to the performance of noble deeds, the White Knight rides out to slay the dragon. If his

A crowd of knights in medieval costumes await the coming of the terrible dragon.

A fierce dragon comes out of the forest in the "dragon-sticking" festival at Furth-im-Wald.

first spear-thrust draws dragon's blood, it is believed that the town will be free from aggression for another year.

INTO AUSTRIA

At Passau two tributaries flow into the Danube: the narrow Ilz hurrying down its rocky path from the north, the broad Inn bringing from the southland the ice-cold waters of the Alps. The Inn also brings with it a hint of the lilting charms of Salzburg off in the foothills, with its gay cafés, its festival air, its multitude of church towers and its love of music.

It is here, on a lake near Salzburg, that we find a target range like no other in all the world. For the bullets shot across the lake must hit the water first, then ricochet up to the target on the far side.

Back on the Danube, floating now through Austria, we find a tranquil atmosphere despite the country's troubled recent past. In the villages town bands give concerts in costume, and there are torchlight processions and music and singing in out-of-door cafés.

On the sloping fields, white ox-teams move slowly; the tinkle of cowbells sounds from pasture lands; and atop the slopes loom the heavy, frowning shapes of the medieval castles from which the land was once ruled.

The newly dubbed White Knight slays the dragon, thus saving his town from aggression.

Some of the feudal lords were fine fellows who took seriously their responsibilities as protectors of the poor. But most of them thought of the serfs as less than human. And some were blustering, heartless robber barons like the one who stretched a chain across the river a thousand feet below his castle at Aggstein, to stop every boat that passed. To the captains he gave a rigid choice: pay a stiff fee for freedom or die. Those who refused to, or could not, pay were led up to a high cliff near the castle, and there were given another whimsical choice: jump or starve to death. The ghost of this brutal robber baron is one of the many ghosts haunting the Danube today.

In the town of Schönau, a group of men dance the "Schuhplattler" at a guest house.

At Passau, on the German-Austrian border, the rivers Inn and Ilz flow into the Danube.

There are other, happier spirits on the river—at picturesque Linz, and at Melk, where on certain nights the river glows with the tiny lights of thousands of candles set adrift on wooden chips, and every boat is decked with lanterns to glow against the dark.

Then there is the ghost of King Richard the Lionhearted, haunting the battlements of the castle of Durrenstein, where he was held a captive for ransom on his way home from the Crusades. It was his squire, Blondel, who brought about his rescue. Disguised as a troubadour, he wandered the countryside singing the airs his master loved. At last his devotion was rewarded; for as he strolled, singing, beneath the towers of Durrenstein, a voice from above took up the tune—the voice of the captive King Richard.

So Blondel discovered his missing lord and brought about his ransom and rescue. And perhaps of a summer evening you may still hear among the castle's ruins the lilt of Blondel's seven-hundred-year-old song. For in this land history lives on.

VIENNA, QUEEN OF THE DANUBE

Beyond the rolling green Vienna Woods, at a gap in the hills commanding the Danube valley, lies Vienna the beautiful, with its floodlit buildings, its flashing, leaping fountains and its lavish baroque structures thought by admirers to resemble fountains in stone. In every rich, flowing curve Vienna is reminiscent of the glorious era of the Habsburg dynasty which gave to this proud capital of Austria-Hungary the grandeur it still retains.

Home of the waltz, of the club-like coffee house, of pastry and tortes, and of coffee high-piled with whipped cream, Vienna hums, with a tap of the toe and a graceful nod of the head, the music of the masters who made the city their home: Beethoven,

The Danube sweeps past the ruins of many old castles as it passes through Austria.

Mozart, Haydn, Schubert, Brahms, Mahler, and by no means least, the beloved waltz king Johann Strauss. On autumn weekends the Viennese, bidden by bundles of hay tied to poles in front of the taverns, wander out to taste the new wine. The following spring they gather again at village cafés to sample the vintage of the previous fall, and to lift their voices in song.

Vienna has suffered. The first World War cost her empire. Struggling back from a terrible depression, she was overwhelmed by the Nazi tide, and after the second World War was occupied by four armies for a number of years. But again she is rebuilding. Her beautiful Ringstrasse still circles the old city, Inner Town. Seen from the wooded hills to the west, the Ring forms a lovely semi-circle of lights, backing up to the Danube Canal,

The "Statsoper," the State Opera House, is one of the many baroque buildings of Vienna.

across which rises the lively Prater with its continuous fun fair.

So with the song of Vienna still ringing in our ears, we drift on down the river, brown and heavy here with its burden of silt from a hundred hills, past low spurs of the Alpine chain and the Carpathian Mountains to the north, and out into the plains of Hungary.

THE PLAINS OF HUNGARY

On the banks, strips of bleak, plowed earth mark the boundary, dotted with rickety watch-towers, prowled by guards with fierce dogs. To the north rise small mountains crowned by royal palaces, but these palaces are but ghosts of the past, for the plains and hills of Hungary are divided by the iron curtain of communism.

Here the river flattens and widens out, its banks screened with reeds in which herons nest in the shade of bending willow trees. Wherever the ground rises ever so slightly, the slow river drifts lazily around, dividing into several channels with the rising ground forming small islands in midstream. This whole great plain of Hungary was once, in ages past, a mountain-bordered inland sea. But the Danube current burst the mountain barrier to the east, draining the sea; now the plain is a sea of grass and grain.

The people of Vienna enjoy their social life outdoors, as in this suburban wine garden.

The farms here are more primitive, the villages quiet and turned in upon themselves, the small windows of their houses opening onto enclosed courtyards while blank walls face the streets once patrolled by the hated Turkish conquerors.

Past the old Magyar capital of Pozsony we go; it was later called Bratislava, and was re-named Pressburg by the Germans, typical of the Danube's many changes of nationality.

Soon on the right bank, among the last spurs of the dwindling Alpine chain, we see the city of Buda rise, its old mansions and palaces lining hilly, cobbled streets. On the lower left bank stretches Pest, the modern, industrial half of the twin-city capital, Buda-pest. Behind it the land flows away to the "puszta," the wide plains of the dashing Hungarian cowboys of old.

A half dozen bridges of unusual grace join the two halves of Budapest, once thought by many travelers to be the most enchanting of Europe's capitals, now scarred and saddened by war and its aftermath. Halfway between lies Margareten Island, a delightful pleasure spot with meadows, woods, flower gardens, bubbling springs and outdoor cafés.

THROUGH THE IRON GATES

Soon the river turns southward into Yugo-slavia, cutting through the Backa, wheat land considered the most fertile of Danubian soil. We do not see the capital, Belgrade, but it stands on a hilltop not far away, a city site sixteen times destroyed and still more often captured through a turbulent Balkan history, and less than a hundred years ago still a stronghold of the Ottoman Turks.

In the unpainted villages along the river men can still be seen occasionally wearing the baggy Turkish trousers with their thick folds between the legs and sandals with upturned toes. A few last castles appear, dot-

This Danube cruise ship, the "Johann Strauss," is named for Vienna's waltz king.

ting hilltops of the Transylvanian Alps, and then we reach the first of two dangerous stretches to be navigated. This is the steep, rocky defile of Kazan, where the waters, locked between precipitous rock walls, swirl 150 feet deep and the currents are terrible.

Not far beyond comes the second—the gorge which the Danube has cut through the Carpathian Mountains to drain that ancient inland sea which once spread over the Hungarian plain. Here the river, again hemmed in by jagged rocks, races in rapids through the Iron Gate which marks the Yugoslav-Romanian border. Around these rapids the Romans built a canal to ease their river traffic through, especially ships bound upstream. But today, with the turbulent international situation, there is little traffic here.

ON TO THE SEA

Released from the Iron Gate, the river relaxes and spreads out with a sigh in its broad bed. Here it marks the border between two Balkan lands. To the north lie the flat marshes of Romania, with a few villages and scattered fishermen's huts among the river reeds. To the south rise the low heights of Bulgaria, crowned with small towns; but even where these towns face Romanian villages across the wide river, there is seldom a connecting ferry. This is a true border.

Bulgaria, a brooding land released from Turkish domination only in 1878, after 500 years of Turkish rule, does not consider itself a Danubian land, despite its river boundary, for only a few short, unimportant streams flow down from its mountains into the Danube. The two important rivers of Bulgaria empty southward into the Aegean Sea.

As we turn north into Romania, we find busier, livelier towns, but we realize that our journey down the river has also been a journey backward into time. This is a land more closely bound to the old ways of Asia than to modern Europe. We see high boots, fur hats, even some fezzes and turbans, and the bulbous towers of Eastern Orthodox churches.

Here the river feathers out into many shallow branches, wandering through the reeds of a marshy delta which is a wilderness of mud bars, lazy channels and low islands on which oaks and beeches rustle their leaves above nodding willows. Here, had we time, we might see wild boars and wolves; we do glimpse some pelicans diving for fish.

The Danube now reaches the end of its long journey. The long pent-up waters—waters from deep Alpine lakes and snow-fed mountain streams, from uplands steeped in history, from a thousand valley farmlands—all these waters pour into the Black Sea.

SWITZERLAND
People of the Mountains

IN HISTORY and tradition, Europe is a continent of kings and castles—and of war. But long ago, in the shadow of ancient monarchies, upon a groundwork of bitter internal warfare and diversity of race, language and religion, a democracy was founded. That democracy still lives and flourishes today, and its people, secure behind the protective granite ramparts of the Alps, have not heard the sound of battle in more than a hundred years. Our story is of these people and of this lovely mountain homeland of the Swiss.

A LAND DIVIDED

Switzerland is a very small, landlocked nation, a land of lakes and mountains, of green valleys and fertile pastures, of barren peaks and rushing waterfalls. The frosty range of the Alps dominates the landscape; more than three-fifths of the surface of Switzerland is covered with rocky spurs and frozen spires, with glaciers and crevasses, chasms and crags.

Set in among the mountains are the smaller areas of the valleys, softer, milder in their beauty than the mountains, but quite their equal in charm. Here soft green meadows carpet the gentler slopes, winding streams sparkle between flower-strewn banks, and quiet blue lakes reflect the towering grandeur of the peaks.

It is in the lower land, often on the shores of the blue lakes, that the cities of Switzerland are located—Lucerne, Geneva, Zurich. And lovely cities they are. In the higher valleys, small villages are tucked away. And because of the mountains surrounding them, these villages are rather completely cut off from the cities, and even from each other.

During the winters, snow makes travel impractical for the villagers, despite the wonderfully efficient 3,000 miles of modern railroads and highways. During other seasons, the villagers must work far too hard at maintaining their high standard of living to have time for little pleasure trips to other parts of the country. Thus we find the customs and traditions of the people—and even their languages—changing from village to village.

Four languages are spoken in Switzerland, none of them truly Swiss; and in addition there are numerous dialects. Only about one per cent of the people still cling exclusively to Romansh, the oldest tongue in Switzerland, a Latin dialect which has remained unchanged since Roman times. About three-fourths of the people speak Swiss-German; the rest, French or Italian. And in addition, English is spoken by most people.

Some of Switzerland is Catholic, some is Protestant. Bloody religious wars have been fought between these groups in times past.

The mountain ramparts of Switzerland shield it from the outside world.

The goats are herded by a young man who is chosen to serve for an entire year.

But today they live peaceably together, deeply united in a strong love of country.

Let us visit these people of the mountains in one of their secluded villages. And let it represent to us all the villages of Switzerland as we follow its people through a busy year.

VILLAGE LIFE

Here is the village, pretty as a picture. It is no wonder that Swiss villages have so often been painted and photographed; for they have the special charm that comes from im-

maculate housekeeping inside and out, from that extra bit of loving care only devoted householders and skilled craftsmen can supply. Everywhere the gables of the houses—steep gables, planned so heavy snows will slide easily from the roofs—are carved with loving care. Often the windows hold boxes filled with carefully tended flowers—geraniums and begonias, perhaps. Perhaps a lattice frame carries flowering vines up the side of a house. Or the walls of homes and barns may be painted with religious pictures or old sayings. The particular kind of decoration used depends on the locale; but the warmth of devotion to home and village is everywhere evident.

There are few luxuries, few modern conveniences in the village; work done by hand is slow, and there is little time to waste. Even the children are busy, and it seems the busiest of them all is the lad elected to serve as village goatherd, for early each morning it is his job to collect all the goats in the village and drive them out to pasture. There he watches them all through the day, counting noses at intervals. If one turns up missing, the goat boy will scramble far and wide over rocks, risking any hazard. He is responsible for every member of his flock, and to lose one of them would be unthinkable. For his devoted labors he receives a small wage and a lunch supplied by a different family each day.

Back in the village, on washday the central fountain becomes the village laundry. On baking day the village oven, a dome-shaped affair, may hold a town-sized supply of loaves of bread. The women prepare their dough at home, and carry the shaped loaves

Swiss homes are rich with hand-wrought detail, demonstrating skill in carving.

on long wooden boards down to the community oven. The children are kept busy on baking days fetching armloads of kindling and wood to feed the oven's fires. One baking may have to last for a number of weeks, and before another baking day comes along, the last of the bread will be hard as a board; but to many mountain dwellers it has the flavor and texture of home.

SPRING FESTIVAL

Cooking and washing go on year round, but certain activities in the village vary from season to season. The year begins properly in the spring, when the first soft winds come up from the south, thawing and loosening the heavy drifts of snow. As the white blanket

Each day the young goatherd leads his charges up to the green grass of the mountain pasture.

With all this beauty in store, the villagers are, naturally enough, eager to hasten the coming of spring. On the first of March the children harness themselves with bells—cowbells, sleighbells, harnessbells—swung from shoulder yokes or hung around their necks. The oldest boy is the leader, the make-believe cowherd. The younger children play at being the cows; with bells tinkling and

The young girls of the village carry home huge, warm loaves of fresh bread baked in the community oven.

The community laundry, usually at the town's central fountain, is a lively place.

melts away from the high slopes, primroses, anemones, soldanellas and gentians burst into bloom. Higher still the velvety edelweiss is found; and some weeks later slope after slope will be covered with nodding blankets of crocuses, breathtaking in their loveliness.

Leading the cows up to the mountain pastures is a happy village ceremony.

The herds delight in the sweet new young grasses of the high mountain meadows.

clanging noisily, they run here and there, while the leader searches for his "herd." There is much shouting and laughter and waving of sticks, and the children are rewarded with gifts of nuts and fruits for their good work in raising a joyful noise to remind the old gods of the mountains that the time has come for them to send the spring again.

Even in the cities there are festivals for spring, with floats and costumes and merry-making in the streets. In the city of Zurich a huge bonfire is built in the town square to symbolize the hoped-for end to winter. The season is personified as a huge ugly figure called the Böög.

SUMMER PASTURE

As spring settles in and climbs the higher slopes, spreading a green carpet of juicy grasses and herbs, comes the time to move the cows to the high pasture. In some valleys whole families move with their herds to small stone huts near the summer grazing lands. The village teacher may have to move with them, for according to Swiss education laws, if there are ten or more children of school age about, there must be a classroom.

In most valleys, however, including our village, the tasks of herding and dairying are divided among the villagers. Thus a few cowherds drive the cattle to the pasturelands and care for them there. Others gather the milk, keeping careful track of the amount produced by each owner's cows; still others churn the butter, make the cheese and keep the accounts. At the season's end, the produce is divided with fairness to all.

When the cows are led from their winter sheds to make the ascent to the high Alpine pastures (to the Swiss the word "Alps"

The young kid has found a friendly companion in this small Swiss child.

The big bells come out of the barn when springtime lures the cows up the mountains.

means not mountains but upland pastures) the whole village turns out in festive dress, and even the animals are wreathed with flowers. Often the village priest is present to bless the departing herd. There is always an accordion player around; sometimes there are several musicians to add to the gaiety. And there are bells—not just cowbells, but special, elaborate ones.

On the way, the traditional cow fight is held; it usually does not take much urging to get the cows to pushing and butting, and the winner of the battle is declared leader of the herd. When all her rivals have been butted or chased away, she is garlanded with flowers; and a milking stool is placed between her horns as a sign that she is queen.

CHEESE MAKING

Back in the village the official cheese maker, elected to his post and paid by the villagers for his work, has set up shop in a village hut with his helpers, and equipment that is simple and old. As the herd's milk is brought down to them, they skim off the cream,

churn it into butter, and press the butter into loaves. They scrub out the great wooden cheese barrels, pour the skimmed milk into large pots or vats, and stir in a curdling agent to speed the separation of thick curds from thin, watery whey.

After a suitable interval, a sheet of loose-woven cheesecloth is dipped into the vat and swished around until it holds most of the curds. Then up comes the cheesecloth, and the last of the whey drains out. The new cheese is then aged in wooden molds.

To separate the curds from the whey, the cheese is stirred as it cooks in huge vats.

Finished cheeses are sorted by size and then are stored for aging on cellar shelves.

Haying time takes an entire Swiss family, armed with scythes, into the fields.

The fragrant hay is gathered in great bundles for transportation into town.

Dated and labeled, the cheeses in their molds are stored for aging on cellar shelves, to be divided at the season's end among the villagers whose cows supplied the milk.

HARVESTTIME

Only a small portion, at best, of Switzerland's land can be used for farming, so none of the usable acreage is allowed to go to waste. There are vineyards tucked among the rocks, with wooden troughs, running cross country for miles, to irrigate the vines. There are cornfields perched on hilly slopes, fields of wheat and pastures of hay.

In these cramped, uneven, rock-bound, sloping fields, large-scale modern farm machinery would be quite out of place. The soil is still tilled and cultivated by hoe as it has been for long generations past. The work is hard and time-consuming, but all hands in the family do their share. And probably nowhere in the world do the farmers make their acres provide a richer yield.

Late summer brings haymaking time, and out to the slopes go the families, armed with long-handled, curved-bladed scythes, and with bundles of lunch. The hay they cut will provide winter feed for the livestock, so every bundle counts. The bundles are gathered on pole sleds, secured with ropes, and drawn by patient horses down the long hillsides to the waiting village barns.

Then there is wheat to be harvested—cut and stacked and bundled, and threshed with age-old paddles called "flegels." Then it's off to the mill with its old water wheel; and to the squeal of wooden cogs and the rattle of ratchets is added the soft whisper of the grain as it swishes down into baskets and sacks. The crop has been good; so even after leaving a generous portion to pay the miller, each family will have plenty of flour for bread in the snowbound months ahead.

THE RETURN OF THE HERD

Against the night sky, the mountains tower darkly above the village. And high on a dark, craggy shoulder, the light of a bonfire flares. As the villagers gather to watch, the ball of fire is pushed from its bed and sent tumbling down from the lofty crag with wild spattering of yellow flame! That is a signal. The herds are coming home!

Next day, toward midafternoon, the air is filled with the tinkle of bells. Louder and louder the merry sound grows as the cows near the home village. From the valley below, the watchers can see their animals etched against the sky, mooing and jostling as if indeed they were eager to be home.

Soon the valley echoes to the blast of the alpenhorn, that long, widemouthed, curved wooden horn whose song is so dear to the Swiss. And at its call all the villagers assemble to celebrate the cows' return. To the

The sound of the long, wooden alpenhorns floats far across the wide valleys.

The village choir sings the old familiar songs to help celebrate the return of the herd.

Folk dancing by the town's inhabitants is a lively part of the Guarda Festival.

moos of the cows and the jangle of their bells are added the shouting and the singing of the children, the laughter and applause of the grown-up villagers as they watch the lively wrestling matches and amateur shows, and the full-throated calls of the yodelers.

There is usually a picnic, with dancing and singing. And the cheeses are brought up from their cellars to be sampled and divided up. For harvesttime is a grand time for celebrating; and cheese is the harvest of the herd.

Out from the cupboards come the treasured old costumes—some with marvelous headpieces or masks. There are lantern light processions; there is dancing in the square for all the family to enjoy. There are gymnastic contests, choral singing contests, and various games of skill. "Hornussen" is a favorite game, played only when the harvest is in and fields are bare. It involves whacking a solid rubber puck with a long ashen club, trying to drive it into the opposing team's goal—it is a fast, energetic game.

THE LONG WINTER

Soon after harvesttime, the mists steal in; leaves color and drop off the trees, shivered by chill winds; and the first snow flurries drift down the slopes. Soon the village is dressed in winter white, and the pattern of life settles down to its leisurely winter tempo.

With farms and pastures snowbound, attention turns to indoor crafts. In many a home the shuttle moves swiftly back and forth on the loom, as the housewife weaves sturdy and handsome cloth. Knitting needles click in quiet corners, and bright threads flash as deft-fingered women embroider elaborate patterns in delicately spaced stitches.

Autumn brings new, although short-lived, beauty to the valley, before winter comes.

During the winter, wood carving and other crafts keep the housebound families busy.

Mountain climbing is popular in Switzerland.

Sharp knives slice into soft wood as the menfolk whittle out toys and boxes; even the children are busy with needle or knife or paintbrush these days. For that loveliest of feast days, Christmas, is coming. And in every Swiss homestead excitement begins to mount. There are gifts to be fashioned for Christmas-week giving, as well as extra goods to be made for sale in town.

In the kitchens there's a rich and spicy fragrance as tins of Christmas cookies come hot from the oven, tempting the children to sample each tin, though they are on their best behavior, it seems.

Behavior is important these days, for on December 6th comes St. Nicholas' Day. And it is well known that St. Nicholas, or Klaus, as he is often called, will not only bring gifts on his name day to the good children, but punishment to any who have, alas, been bad. And sure enough, when he comes at last, wearing a long white beard and flowing robe, he carries tasty fruits and nuts in one hand, in the other a long stick! Saint Klaus is followed in the procession by a group of helpers in white robes, wearing on their heads huge headpieces, often decorated with elaborate village scenes. Here in miniature you may see the cows driven to pasture, the

cheese maker at work in his hut, or a logging scene in the timber country. And sometimes the mask is lighted with candles inside.

There are Christmas trees in Switzerland on Christmas Eve, decorated with candles, apples, nuts and cookies. Families gather to sing Christmas carols, to serenade their neighbors or to go for a sleigh ride; and they all meet at church for the Christmas mass.

So without the flurry of shopping, and the excitement and crowds of the big department stores, without the expense of elaborate decorations or boughten fun, the warmth and happiness of Christmas steal over the village as softly as a fall of Christmas snow.

Oh, there is more excitement than this to be found in Switzerland. There are sleighing races at the big resorts, skiing (a fairly recent import from Norway), bobsledding down ice-smooth tracks. There is mountain climbing among the snowy peaks. But the folk of the village are content with the peaceful, busy, even tenor of their lives. They are a fortunate people indeed, at peace with themselves and with the world, safe at home in their beloved land of mountains.

THE SWISS FAMILY ROBINSON

THE WORLD has always been full of ordinary people who live in houses on the ground and never dream of living in a tree top. But the father of the Swiss family was no ordinary man.

He had his own ideas about many things. For one, he disliked the noisy crowds and the stale air of city streets. He also felt that people did not live the way they were meant to on this rich, bountiful earth.

The world was so big a place, the father argued, that surely there must be some new land where he could find a better life for his family. North, south, east, or west—which way should he go? Perhaps the travel books would tell him.

The family had a mother, too. For a long time, she was happy to remain in Switzerland, clucking and fussing like a worried mother hen over her growing sons.

Fritz, the oldest son, was nineteen. He was sturdily handsome, with broad shoulders and a powerful chest. Few young men could have been better equipped than Fritz for facing life in a wilderness.

Ernst, who was eighteen, was just the opposite of Fritz. He was thin and had a faraway look in his eyes. He was more of a dreamer and a student.

Francis, the youngest, was eight. Round faced and restless, he was always wishing that something exciting would happen.

If not for Napoleon Bonaparte, the mother might have been happy to live in Switzerland forever. But when Napoleon plunged all of Europe into war, millions of men went into battle. And the mother, fearful for the grown men in her family, started showing a keen interest in her husband's travel books.

After some deliberation, they decided to move the whole family to New Guinea.

The father's heart brimmed with happiness, when a few weeks later, the Swiss family stood on the deck of a small merchantman. The way ahead seemed long. But somehow the parents felt they and their sons were headed in the right direction.

Day after day, the ship sailed south and the days stretched into weeks. One day, near the Malay Peninsula they sighted a pirate ship bearing down on them. At this, Captain Willhelm of the merchantman changed course abruptly, and crowded on all canvas in an attempt to flee.

As they raced southward under full sail, the wind rose and the waves grew rougher. Soon a gale was blowing.

On the fifth day of the storm, the captain ordered the Swiss family below to their cabin. A short time later, there was a sharp crack—and the mainmast fell with a thunderous crash, pulling sails and rigging down with it.

On the sixth day, there were no signs of life above deck. The ship was dying—her seams opened to the seas, her wheel spinning madly from side to side. Suddenly the prow scooped into an oncoming wave, sending tons of water hurtling back along the deserted decks.

In crashing through the deck, the mainmast had jammed their cabin door—and the Swiss family was trapped below.

With Fritz and Ernst helping him, the father worked feverishly. If they did not force the door open in time, the cabin would become their tomb.

"Somebody, get us out of here!" called the father.

A lantern swinging wildly from a peg on the ceiling sent eerie shadows racing across the cabin. The mother felt sick with fear. Bracing herself against the lurching bunk, she tightened her grip on little Francis.

Then, suddenly, the ship struck something with a rolling, ripping jar. The impact of the crash sent luggage flying across the cabin, and hurled the lantern to the floor.

There was darkness all around the Swiss family.

EVERY MAN FOR HIMSELF

The ship lay under the dark sky, lodged fast where it had struck a huge jagged rock. Pounding waves crashed against the hull all night long. But by morning, the storm had ended. Below decks, the Swiss family forced their cabin door open at last.

"Captain Willhelm? Anybody! Helloa there!" called Fritz.

But only an echo answered; nothing else. *"Helloa there . . . !"*

"They've abandoned ship," said Ernst, his eyes gleaming with excitement. "They've got no claim to it now . . . it's ours!"

The mother's eyes widened. "I can't believe they'd just go off and leave us. Something must have happened."

"They thought she was going down—it was every man for himself," the father said grimly.

The Swiss family found the deck cluttered with torn sails and shattered portions of masts. Little Francis stared about, whistling and beaming. What a wonderful mess!

Then, hearing a dull booming sound, they all moved over to the gunwale. The sound was made by surf breaking on a maze of coral reefs in the distance. Behind the reefs, they could see a palm-fringed island.

The father said, "At least we're not too far from land."

"Then . . . there's hope?" the mother asked.

"We can build a raft and get to shore . . . at least I'm sure of that," said the father.

At this moment, Francis, who had wandered off, called to them: "Come here, look!"

Quickly, they joined Francis at the open main hatch. Staring down into the hold, they saw a cow, a calf, three goats, a donkey, a couple of old sows, and several crates of ducks, chickens, and geese. Feed was scattered about, and the cow was standing knee-deep in water on the lower deck.

The mother shook her head. "Poor things. They probably had a worse time of it than we did."

The father looked grave. "How does it look?" Fritz asked. "Are we pretty solid on the rocks?"

The father frowned. "I don't know how much time we've got here . . ."

He meant to say more, but at that moment Francis flew out of the companionway, clutching the brass-studded collars of two huge, galloping dogs.

The mother screamed. "Francis! Let go!"

He let go reluctantly; and the father grabbed him as he spun across the wet and slippery deck.

"Gosh," sighed Francis, gazing fondly after the dogs, "Duke and Turk sure were glad to see me."

The family spent the rest of the morning getting ready for the trip to shore. Down in the captain's cabin, Ernst had found a compass and a sextant. "Suppose it's a deserted island. I can figure out where we are, when I learn how to use this sextant."

Busy gathering up muskets and pistols, the father nodded.

Ernst laid the sextant down and moved to

a small organ fastened to the wall. Experimentally, he played a few notes. Then, moving on, he opened the lid of a cabinet.

"Come here," he said. "Look."

The cabinet was packed with signal flags. A diagram on the underside of the lid showed the meaning of the different flags. Running his finger down the diagram, Ernst said, "Don't you think we ought to put up a distress signal?"

The father smiled grimly. "Anybody who sees a ship breaking up on a rock could *guess* it's in trouble without a flag."

Up on deck, Fritz was stripped to the waist, sawing a huge barrel in half. Other tubs and barrels were already bound together, and a tub-raft was beginning to take shape.

"I still don't see how we're going to carry the animals," said Fritz, frowning.

"We're not," the father said quietly.

Fritz gulped. "But we can't just go off and leave them here!"

The father's face grew pale. Turning away, he said gruffly, "When your mother and your brothers are safe on land, *then* you can talk to me about animals! Not before!"

A few hours later, the raft was bouncing in the waves, loaded with supplies. The mother, the father, and Francis sat in three of the tubs; and Ernst sat in another, holding a rope and trying to keep the raft in close to the ship.

The two dogs, Duke and Turk, stood on deck as Fritz began crawling down the rope.

Francis called urgently, "The dogs, Fritz! You forgot them!"

The father tightened his jaw. "They're not coming," he said.

"They're my dogs!" cried Francis scrambling up out of his barrel. "I found them!"

"Francis, sit down!" the father said sharply. "The dogs probably weigh more than any of us. We'd sink for sure!"

Francis settled back into his tub with a grimace, and Fritz and Ernst cast off. As the raft, pitching in the waves, pulled away from the ship, the dogs ran back and forth along the deck, barking and whining.

Surreptitiously, Francis motioned with one hand to call them to him. Duke and Turk leaped over the side and started swimming toward the raft.

Francis said innocently, "Here come the dogs."

Now the raft moved out to catch the full brunt of the churning waves. Pitching and bobbing, it swung wildly about.

The two dogs tumbled about in the raging waters, whining pitifully. The mother whispered. *"Do something!"*

"No!" The father shook his head. "We can't take a chance of upsetting the raft." His face flaming, he continued his efforts to get the raft into calm water.

But the whines of the drowning dogs swelled louder and louder in his ears. And suddenly he found himself reaching out to pull Turk aboard. As the heavy dog started over the edge, the father's tub went partly under water. He worked desperately to get the weight more evenly distributed. At the other end of the raft, Fritz and Ernst were pulling Duke aboard.

Water poured into their tubs, and they tipped dangerously. As Fritz pulled the struggling dog toward the center of the raft, Ernst tried to block the inpouring waves with his body. Just as the entire raft seemed on the verge of breaking apart, the dogs moved inward by themselves.

With everybody working frantically to clear the tubs, they reached calm water at last. The mother sighed with relief.

Smiling ruefully, the father said, "Let's get to shore. I wouldn't dare pray for any *more* miracles . . . all in one day."

PIRATES

As the Swiss family neared shore, Fritz and Ernst jumped into the surf to help pull the raft inland. A moment later, Francis scrambled out.

He raced off down the beach, followed by Duke and Turk. Flocks of pelicans and colorful macaws rose into the air, screaming and croaking their surprise at such unexpected company.

The father carried his wife up to where the sand was dry. Pointing to some towering palms, he said:

"At least we'll have enough food. Those are coconuts."

After a quick glance upward, the mother turned her gaze anxiously down the beach.

"No sign of any people," said the father.

The mother frowned. There was no sign of Francis either.

But then she saw him about fifty yards away, emerging from the jungle astride a huge, slowly crawling tortoise.

"Francis!" she called, the sharpness of her voice softened by relief. "Come here!"

As soon as the whole family was together, the father said, "Now the first thing we do is unload the raft."

The mother shook her head. "No," she said quietly. "Not the *first* thing."

For a moment the father was baffled. Then he understood. They all dropped to their knees and began to pray.

That night, while the boys slept, the mother and father talked together.

"We'll get to New Guinea yet, you'll see," said the father. "And meanwhile, we're not *too* badly off! We're alive; we have our family together . . . food to eat . . ."

Just then a tiger roared somewhere in the darkness; and the mother shuddered. "I will pray for a ship," she said, "with every breath I take."

The next day she and Francis stayed ashore, while the father rowed out to the wreck with Fritz and Ernst.

Fritz at once started fashioning life preservers out of kegs for the animals. Suddenly Ernst gave a shout, "There's a ship!"

Ernst was perched halfway up a shattered mast. He was waving toward the horizon and calling wildly, "Ship ahoy! Ahoy there!"

The father had found a telescope, and he raised it to his eye—but a moment later his face grew grimly sober.

He spoke rapidly. "It's the pirate ship that chased us into the storm. Ernst, come down from the mast. Better keep down, Fritz; try not to let them see you . . ."

Now all three were huddled behind the gunwale. The telescope up to his eye again, the father said, "They're bringing a cannon into position . . . they're preparing to fire."

Fritz glanced about. Their "ship" had a cannon too! "At least we can argue the point with them a little," he said.

"Do you know how to fire it?" asked Ernst.

"I think so."

The father rushed off, calling back over his shoulder, "I'll get a keg of powder. Ernst, see if you can find any kind of rags we can use for wadding."

The father had just returned with a powder keg when the pirates fired their first shot. As the ball whistled overhead, Fritz said, "That was just to warn us."

The father's face was white. "*We'll* have only *one* shot," he said. "Let's wait until we can't possibly miss."

"How are these for wadding?" asked Ernst, rushing back with an armload of flags and banners.

"Good!" said Fritz. "Rip them into ribbons!"

Ernst and the father dropped to their knees. The father was about to tear a yellow banner with a large black ball in the center of it—when suddenly he stopped, his brow furrowed with thought. A moment later, he got to his feet and moved off, taking the banner with him.

By now, Fritz was ramming a load of powder into the muzzle. Ernst moved in with some ripped bits of flags, and they both poked the wadding down the muzzle, tapping it gently.

Fritz swallowed hard. "Let's see how lucky we are," he said.

He bent to take a sighting. But then, squinting along the muzzle, he saw the pirate ship wheeling about in the wind, moving *away* from them.

Fritz rubbed his eyes with disbelief. "They're . . . leaving!"

"D-do you suppose they *saw* us loading the cannon? And th-they got scared off?" stammered Ernst.

Fritz snorted. "*Pirates?* Scared off . . . by three of us, and *one* cannon?"

Then, turning to the father who had just rejoined them, Fritz asked, "Do you know what they're up to?"

Instead of replying with words, the father turned his eyes up toward the top of the shattered mast. Staring up, his sons saw the yellow banner with the black-ball center fluttering there. Fritz asked, "What's that?"

"Quarantine flag," the father said. "Warning that there's the black death aboard."

The two boys shook their heads in awe at their father's clever strategy. "But how'd you know *that?*" asked Ernst.

With a twinkle in his eye, the father answered, "I do a bit of reading, too, you know."

THE TREE HOUSE

The father had tricked the pirates into sailing away. He was sure that the Swiss family's troubles were over for the day.

On the island, however, Francis had wandered off again . . .

"Francis?" the mother was calling anxiously as she moved toward the jungle fringe at the back of the beach. "Francis, where are you?"

Just then the two dogs came bounding over.

Flanked by the dogs, she moved slowly into the jungle. "Francis? Where are you . . . ?" she called again.

Francis was in a small open area, trying to capture a baby elephant. The elephant loped about, nervously eyeing the bit of sugar in Francis's hand.

"Here, little elephant! Come here. I wouldn't hurt you . . ." crooned Francis as he edged toward a sturdy rope snare spread out in a loop on the ground.

Just then he heard his mother calling. He frowned. Just like a mother to come barging along and frighten off the best and biggest pet a boy could ever hope to catch!

Suddenly the baby elephant seemed almost in a panic. Trumpeting with fright, it started running off, but then skidded to a halt. And then, backing up, it stepped into the snare.

At once Francis gave the rope a pull and quickly tightened the other end about a tree trunk. The rope jerked, and Francis almost lost his hold. The baby elephant, caught by only one leg, was heaving with all its strength, trying to get loose; and it was trumpeting even louder than before.

Moving forward, Francis tied the rope to secure his new pet. He was beaming with triumph when he finished this task. But then, glancing up, he saw the reason for the elephant's panic.

An enormous tiger was slinking forward, prepared to spring . . . !

Without thinking, Francis picked up a rock and hurled it. "You get out of here!" he cried.

At this moment, Duke and Turk burst into the clearing. Working from two sides, they moved in to worry the tiger. The big cat snarled viciously and lashed out with a paw. Growling and barking, the dogs darted in and out, never letting up for a moment.

The mother reached the clearing just in time to see the tiger turn and lope off, leaving the dogs to lick their wounds.

Tears streamed down her face as she knelt to hug first Duke, then Turk. "You wonderful, wonderful dogs," she said gratefully.

"They sure showed that old tiger who was boss!" said Francis.

At this, the mother looked up and said sternly, "Francis, you could have been killed, walking off that way."

Francis hung his head.

"Well, Francis, don't you have anything at all to say?" demanded the mother angrily.

"I'm sorry I did it," he said. "But . . ."

The mother was watching him closely. Suddenly she smiled. "But what?" she asked.

"But . . ." said Francis, ". . . can I still keep the baby elephant, anyhow?"

And so Francis kept his new pet, "anyhow." And the father of the Swiss family thought of a way of using the baby elephant to help them build a tree house.

First the father found a suitable tree—an enormous *banyan* with thick, wide, strong, spreading branches.

Then he made a harness and ran some rope from it through a pulley fastened to the base of the tree. And as the harnessed elephant moved in a circle, straining to get the chunk of sugar cane held out as bait by Francis—the first bundle of planks was hoisted up into the tree.

A few days later, coming from the beach with a load of planks, the father stopped to mop his brow. Tilting back his head, he gazed with pride at the almost finished tree-platform that Fritz and Ernst were building.

"Well?" he asked his wife. "What do you think of it? It will make a good safe home for us."

The mother frowned. "I'd like it a lot better if tigers couldn't climb trees."

"They won't climb *this* one by the time we're finished," said the father with a smile. "You've probably never *seen* such a house as this is going to be."

"I'm sure of it," the mother said curtly.

Still looking up at the tree, the father asked, "Didn't you ever *dream* of having a home in a tree top?"

The mother was in no mood to speak of dreams. "You must think we're going to be here a long time," she said.

The father said, "I have no way of knowing, my dear . . . but we can't spend our days just sitting on the beach, waiting for a ship to come by."

"But there *could* be a ship, couldn't there?"

"Of course."

"Then—don't you think we'd be better off to light the signal fire?"

At this, the father's face grew grave. "And just forget about the pirates?" he said.

"Maybe they won't be back," the mother said doggedly. "Maybe we could get away with it."

The father shook his head. "We can't take that chance. Right now being alive is more important than being found."

Soon the main platform was completed. Ratlines, like the threads of an enormous cobweb, led from it up to a smaller platform. And more ratlines led down to the ground.

For the moment, at least, the whole Swiss family was treeborne. Clutching Francis tightly, the mother stared at the ground as if measuring the distance from the main platform.

Pointing to a coil of rope, one end of which was tied firmly to a branch, she said, "Make Francis tie that around his waist . . . just in case he falls."

Disgusted and humiliated, Francis tied the loose end of the rope about his waist.

Just then the father joined the mother on the main platform. Beaming with pride, he guided her toward the edge. "Right there . . ." he said, pointing, "we'll have steps going up to our room."

The mother shook her head. "You'll never get *me* to go way up there, unless you give me some kind of a railing to hold onto."

"Just a *railing?*" cried the father. He seemed shocked by her inability to read the blueprint in his mind. "It will be all enclosed . . . don't you understand? Just like a house."

Shrugging coldly, the mother said, "Come on, Francis. We're going down."

"Aw—please?" begged Francis. "Can't I just stay a minute?"

"He'll be all right," the father said; and with a sigh, the mother started down the ladder.

Left alone, Francis swung moodily in the hammock that Fritz had made. He was wishing, of course, that something exciting would happen.

Just then, glancing up, he saw several small monkeys moving down the ratlines.

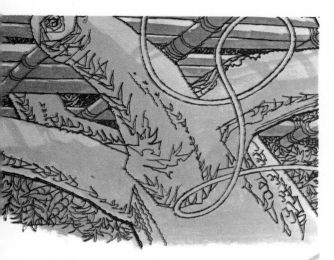

And there was a baby monkey among them.

Francis sat bolt upright. What a perfect pet!

Leaving the hammock, he started inching forward along the ratlines.

"Nice little monkey," crooned Francis. "Here, little monkey. I wouldn't hurt you."

Just then, Ernst called sharply from above, "What are you trying to do?"

At this, all the monkeys tried to scamper away; and Francis sprang into action with a now-or-never desperation. Chasing up the ratlines, he made a frantic lunge for the baby monkey.

There was a wild chattering of protest from all the watching monkeys.

In gaining a pet, however, Francis lost his balance. He fell, snapping the safety rope taut and swinging from side to side like a pendulum.

Ernst rushed down the ratlines from above; and Fritz rushed up from below, followed by the father and the mother.

As they hauled Francis up to the platform, he was clutching the baby monkey.

"You ought to feel the way his heart is beating," he said.

The mother was tight-lipped and shaken. "I could *match* him, beat for beat." Then, she turned grimly to her husband. "Suppose I hadn't just *happened* to insist that Francis tie that rope around his waist?"

The father shrugged; he had no answer.

She went on, "Until you get some railings put up, I don't want Francis back up here . . . and I assure you *I* won't be."

RUNNING OUT OF TIME

The next few months passed very quickly.

They were all so busy, they didn't know where the time went. The father, Fritz, and Ernst worked up in the tree all day.

Cooking and sewing kept the mother busy down at the beach camp. Francis tended the livestock there, wandering off from time to time to add to his rapidly growing collection of pets.

The cow calved, and almost every morning there was another lamb in the sheepfold. The baby elephant grew larger, and so did the baby monkey—and so did the tree house. And at last the day came when it was ready to be inspected by the mother.

"Well, there it is," said the father.

The mother's eyes opened wide with wonder. The house was a masterpiece. Although built of salvaged timber and split bamboo, it had the charm of a Swiss chalet.

With a gallant gesture, the father swept

his wife up into his arms. "An old Swiss custom," he said, "—carrying the bride across the threshold."

At the foot of the tree was a kitchen area sheltered by bamboo screens. A wash basin had been improvised from a huge turtle back. Split-bamboo pipes carried water from a nearby stream to a large barrel equipped with a spigot.

"Ernst dreamed it up . . . Fritz built it," the father said proudly. "Running water, all the latest improvements . . ."

Next he led the mother up to the main room. Hanging pots of flowers added a blaze of color; and decorative dishes and utensils stood on narrow shelves along one wall.

From there, the father moved over to a ship's wheel mounted just beyond the railing. He spun the wheel; and the mother, peering down, saw the bottom section of the stairs rise slowly from the ground.

"When you're in for the night, just turn the wheel and pull your stairs up," said the father. "And you keep out all the wild animals."

Passageways led to two separate sleeping rooms. In their room, the father pulled on a rope—and a section of the roof slid open. "That's so we can lie here and look up at the stars," he said. "Do you like it?"

Her eyes shining with tears, the mother turned to face him. For a long time all she could do was nod.

"It's so wonderful," she said. "I don't deserve it . . ."

Now the Swiss family had their wonderful tree house—but time still passed quickly. Making a forge and a dugout canoe kept their hands busy. And their minds were kept busy by the mystery of the many different kinds of animals.

So far they had identified: tigers, bears, elephants, hyenas, manatees, monkeys, lizards, and ostriches. The mystery was—how had so many different kinds of animals come to be grouped together, all on one island?

"Maybe it *isn't* an island," said Ernst one day. "Why couldn't it be part of the Malay Peninsula?"

Fritz looked up from the dugout canoe he was carving. Glancing over toward where the father was working on the forge, he said in a loud voice, "I know a good way to find *out:* let's try to sail around it. We might even find a village or something . . . some place where ships stop."

Joining them, the father said coldly, "It's no use. You know how your mother feels about that."

Straightening up, Fritz turned and said quietly to his father, "Why don't you talk to Mother again; see if she won't change her mind about our trying to sail around the island?"

The next day dawned warm and bright. Seated on a grassy slope near a pond, the mother watched the father and the boys as they played a game of follow-the-leader.

Fritz swung from one long vine to the next in a succession of graceful arcs. Pausing, he called back, "You've got to take full swings like I did, or it doesn't count."

The others nodded; and Ernst started swinging forward, followed by Francis. Then came the father. Suddenly his vine broke. He swung out and down and—SPLASH—into the pond below.

The boys were still convulsed with laughter as the father, dripping wet, sat down on the grass beside his wife.

"That was very graceful," the mother teased.

"Thank you," he said with a grin. Then, motioning to the area about them, he said, "Isn't this wonderful?"

The mother nodded. For a long moment the father stared thoughtfully into space. "Don't you sometimes feel," he said at last, "that this is the kind of life we were *meant* to live on this earth? Everything we need is

right at our fingertips." Sighing, he went on, "If men would be *satisfied* with just what we have here . . . there wouldn't be any real problems in the world."

"Or any future generations either," the mother added quietly. "There isn't *everything* we need . . . right at our fingertips."

The father looked up sharply. "What are you talking about?"

"This," the mother said. "The island. I know, for *today* it's wonderful. But what about *tomorrow?* And what about our sons? What future is there here for them? Suppose we never get away? And they never have a chance to get married . . ."

Suddenly the father's eyes twinkled. "That's right," he said. "There *aren't* many girls around here, are there?"

"It's nothing to joke about," the mother said unsuspectingly. "Suppose the boys never know what it's like to have a family . . ."

At this, the father gave her a sidelong glance. With a sly smile, he said, "What you're saying, then . . . we ought to make every possible effort to get away from here."

The mother nodded firmly; she was in complete agreement.

"All right," he said. "I'll tell the boys we've decided to let them sail around the coast."

The mother's face turned white. "That's not what I said!"

The father shook his head. "We can't keep putting it off."

"But what do *they* know about outriggers . . . or sailing?" wailed the mother. "Perhaps . . . when the time comes . . ."

"We're running *out* of time," the father said firmly. "You said it yourself—our boys are growing up. They have a life ahead. We can't hold onto them forever."

In a few days the outrigger canoe was ready—and Fritz and Ernst set out. As they paddled away, the father, the mother, and Francis stood on the beach watching them. The canoe grew smaller and smaller. It passed through a gap in the coral reefs, and then the water was empty again.

The father said, "Now just don't worry about it. They'll be back, my dear, before you know it."

The mother nodded. But then, biting her lips, she said, "I hope we're doing the right thing, letting them go."

A FINE FIX

"Look!" cried Fritz. "What's that to starboard? Get your glass!"

They had been skirting the island for days and nights, over wind-swept seas and through calm, sluggish waters. And now, as they neared the rock-strewn entrance to a bay, their sea voyage was coming to an end.

Ernst snatched the telescope and squinted through it. "I see ships," he said. "But I can't tell if there's a village or not . . ."

Taking his turn at the glass, Fritz said, "They look like pirate ships to me." Then, after a pause, "That one . . . I'm *sure* it's the same one we scared off with the quarantine flag."

Fritz brought the outrigger about and steered it toward a narrow gap between the rocks. "Let's try to sneak in a little closer," he said.

But the water around the rocks churned swift and white. Although the boys slashed and fought with their paddles, suddenly they found themselves lifted high into the air by a mountainous swell. A moment later, slammed down hard by the wave, the canoe split apart on a rock, hurling them and all its contents into the surf.

Fritz reached shore first, pulling after him all that he had been able to salvage—a soggy bedroll. When Ernst came ashore, all that he had was the clothes on his back and the compass attached to a thong around his neck.

"It's a fine fix I've got us into," Fritz said grimly.

Using the rocks as cover, the boys inched their way toward a group of trees at the end of the beach. From there, lying flat on their stomachs, they saw two junks anchored in the bay—and on the beach, at least ninety Malaysian pirates engaged in a division of the spoils from their last triumph.

Suddenly Fritz whispered, "Look! Prisoners . . . an old ship captain and a boy!"

At this moment, the two pirate leaders approached the bound prisoners. Passing by the captain, they moved in on the frail young boy crudely dressed in ill-fitting sailor's garb. After feeling his muscles and examining his ears, his eyes, and his teeth, one of them said, "You, boy—you old, how long?"

Addressing the pirate by name, the old captain said, "He is twelve years, Kuala."

Kuala motioned to several of his henchmen; and they started to drag the boy off.

At this, the old captain shouted, "You! Kuala! Wait!"

Turning back, Kuala motioned for the boy to be put down.

"You will want me to write a ransom note," the captain said slowly. "I write . . . my people send money . . . you let me go."

The pirate nodded. "Send plenty money," he said with an evil grin. "You go home."

The captain shook his head. "Keep boy with me," he said firmly, "or I not write note . . . you not get money."

Turning to the others, Kuala explained the problem to them in Malaysian. First he pointed in two directions and shook his head. Then, holding up two fingers tight together, he nodded vigorously.

The other pirate shook his head just as vigorously; he was opposed to the prisoners remaining together. Shouting wildly, he and Kuala and all their henchmen rushed back down the beach to the main body of pirates.

As the shouting and the din increased, Fritz said, "We could sneak in there and set them free before the pirates know what's happening. Come on! It's now or never!"

Creeping up behind the prisoners, Fritz whispered, "Shhh! Don't make a sound. We've come to help you."

As the brothers started working on the thongs, the captain whispered, "They won't harm me . . . I'm valuable for ransom. Get Bertie . . . get the boy free first!"

Fritz motioned for Ernst to help him; and, working together, they soon had Bertie's wrists free. But before they could start on the thongs around his feet, they were all suddenly aware what a strange silence had settled over the pirate beach.

Turning, they saw Kuala pick up a flat stone and spit on one side of it. Then, looking around to make sure the other pirate leader and his henchmen were close to him, Kuala flipped the stone into the air, spinning it like a coin.

The others followed the course of the stone with their eyes, and then hurried to look at it as it landed. As they bent low to inspect it, Kuala and his men sprang upon them with flashing knives.

The treacherous Kuala's sole purpose in flipping the stone had been to catch his opponents kneeling and off guard. And now the entire beach became a seething battlefield.

With difficulty, Fritz and Ernst turned their attention back to Bertie. The moment he was free, they started working with frantic speed on the old captain's thongs.

But just then a sudden wild shouting rose from the beach; and the captain cried, "Get away! Quick! They've seen you! Run! Hurry!"

Kuala and several of his henchmen were rushing toward them; Fritz, Ernst, and Bertie had no choice. Abandoning the captain, they raced toward the jungle-covered hillside.

PURSUIT AND A SURPRISE

With the pirates almost on top of them, Fritz, Ernst, and the frail boy called Bertie rushed headlong through the jungle.

Suddenly Bertie collapsed. Clutching at his side, he sank to the ground. "I can't . . . go on . . . another step," he panted.

Fritz yanked him up impatiently, "Do you think it would hurt less to have a pirate's knife run through you?"

Bertie could only shake his head. "Please . . . you go on . . . I'm sorry."

With a sigh, Fritz released his grip. "Maybe they won't find us right away. We'll let you catch your breath," he said.

"Pirates took your ship?" Ernst asked in a whisper.

Bertie nodded.

Fritz whispered, "What were you? Cabin boy?"

For a moment Bertie hesitated, looking from one to the other. Then, staring down at the ground, he said, "Not really. It was one of my grandfather's ships."

Ernst shook his head in awe. "Just *one* of his ships?"

"The old gentleman on the beach is your grandfather?" asked Fritz.

Bertie nodded again. Then, looking up and

studying the two boys intently, he asked, "Who are you? How did you get here?"

"We were shipwrecked," Ernst started answering. "Our family . . ."

But he broke off as Fritz jabbed him. Someone or something was coming toward them, forcing its way through the thick jungle underbrush.

With hasty hand signals, Fritz motioned a plan of action to Ernst. Then, giving Bertie a shove, he whispered, "Run!"

As Bertie stumbled away, the bushes parted and a huge pirate emerged. He saw Bertie and started in pursuit.

At this moment, Fritz and Ernst leaped forward. Fritz crashed into the pirate at shoulder height; and Ernst hit him at the knees, angling in from the other side. The huge pirate spun crazily and landed in a

heap on the ground. His kris, a short sword with a wavy blade, fell from his hand, and Fritz seized it. Shaking his head groggily, the pirate started to get to his knees. But then Fritz brought the handle of the kris down on his skull, and he gasped and fell.

"Come on!" Fritz whispered. "I hear more of them coming!"

Stopping only long enough to scoop up the pirate's pistol, powder horn, and shot bag, Ernst dashed after his brother in the direction taken by Bertie.

They ran through the jungle until nightfall. Then they climbed a steep slope that led to an open hilltop high above the coast. When at last they reached the top, the sea stretched below them, shimmering in the moonlight. And on the sea were the two pirate ships, moving away from shore.

Fritz gasped, puzzled. "They're *leaving!*"

"It could be a trick to get us back," Ernst said. "You know . . . like the Trojan horse."

Fritz shrugged. "We might as well stay here until daylight." Then, after a pause, he added, "Probably save a lot of time cutting across the island, instead of going back around the beach."

Ernst nodded. "Can't be any question now, about its being an island."

"What about me?" Bertie said suddenly. "What will *I* do?"

Fritz scratched his head. "I guess you'll come with us."

"But my grandfather . . . if they release him . . . he'll come back here looking for me."

Fritz started opening the bedroll, which he had been carrying in a pack on his shoulders. "Don't worry about it," he said gently. "Your grandfather knows you're with us. If we're not here, he'll sail around the island looking for you."

As the brothers finished spreading out the bedroll, Fritz turned to Bertie and said, "Go ahead; you can have the middle."

At this, Bertie backed off, holding his hand up to his mouth. "N-no, thanks. I'll just sit up. I'm not sleepy."

Frowning with annoyance, Fritz ripped off the top blanket and tossed it to him. As the two brothers crawled between the blankets on the warm ground, Bertie retreated to a distant rock.

And there he sat all night long, a small and pathetic figure, with his hands clasped around his knees, and the blanket covering him like a cocoon.

In the morning, moving down the hill, they came to a river bank. Ernst bent over the compass to check the route, then pointed across the river. "That's the direction, right there."

Fritz nodded and, placing his pack and kris on the ground, began to remove his shirt. "Doesn't look as if it'll be over our heads," he said.

Bertie looked horrified. "What are you waiting for, Bertie?" said Ernst.

"It's just until we get across the deep part right here," Fritz explained.

"I can't swim," whimpered Bertie, in a panic.

"I don't think you'll have to," Fritz said firmly. "Now come on; get started."

Trying hard to curb their annoyance, Fritz and Ernst kneeled to remove their shoes. At this moment, Bertie darted forward and seized the pistol, powder horn, and shot bag.

Waving the pistol, he said shrilly, "I'm going back to the beach to wait for my grandfather."

Anger swiftly followed disbelief on the brothers' faces. As one, they moved forward.

"Don't come any closer!" screamed Bertie. "Stay back!"

He was about thirty yards away, and still backing down the trail. "You keep his attention," whispered Fritz. "Let me slip around behind him."

"*I'll* keep his attention all right!" Ernst said grimly. Stooping, he picked up a rock from the trail. Then he seized the buckskin thong that held his pack, and looped and knotted it to make a slingshot. Glaring at Bertie, he started whirling it around his head at terrific speed.

Meanwhile, Fritz, darting from rock to tree to shrub, was moving rapidly and warily in a flanking movement.

Ernst called, "You! Bertie! Drop that pistol now . . . or I'll let this go! Drop it!"

Just then Fritz made a grab at the pistol from behind. Glimpsing him, Bertie started whirling, and accidentally squeezed the trigger.

As the shot kicked up dust between his feet, Ernst for the first time became overwhelmingly angry. He stalked forward with cold fury, his hands curled into jagged fists.

But Fritz had already hurled Bertie to the ground. And although Bertie bit, kicked, scratched, and pulled hair, there was no question as to the outcome of the struggle. In fact, Fritz's fist was already cocked for the knockout blow to the chin—when suddenly Bertie's cap fell off, revealing a crop of coarsely-clipped but definitely feminine hair.

As Ernst came running up, eager for revenge, Fritz was motionless, his fist frozen in mid-air.

"Let me at him!" Ernst cried. "I'll teach him to shoot at me."

Holding Ernst back, Fritz said in a strained voice, "It was my fault the gun went off. She didn't mean to fire."

"I don't care!" Ernst shouted. "I could have been killed!" But then, suddenly stopping and gulping, he asked, "What did you say? *She* didn't mean . . ."

Fritz nodded dazedly. "That's right. It's a girl."

WORSE AND WORSE

"But why should a girl dress like that?" said Ernst, aghast.

"Because of the pirates," Bertie said between sobs. "My grandfather cut my hair . . . he didn't want them to know . . ."

Then she smiled for the first time. "By the way," she said, "my real name is Roberta."

After an awkward moment during which everyone seemed at a loss for words, Fritz said, "Now that we know . . . we'll try to make it easy for you, as much as we can."

The trek that lay ahead of them was long and difficult. After crossing the river, they had to make their way through a treacherous swamp. Wet and miserable, they sloshed along through knee-deep water, slapping futilely at hordes of gnats.

Roberta plodded on, trying her best to keep up.

Once, feeling something wiggle under her hand, she pulled it from the muck. A salamander squirmed out from between her fingers.

A few moments later, she saw a tree branch breaking under the weight of a huge, dragon-like iguana lizard.

As the iguana plopped into the water beside her, Roberta started sobbing hysterically. At once Fritz moved to her side. "He won't hurt you; now come on!" Fritz said sharply.

Later, as they moved single-file through muck almost up to their chests, Fritz, who was in the lead, suddenly vanished.

He came up from the ooze, filthy and spitting. As soon as he reached firmer ground, he hacked two branches with his kris. Throwing them into the bog where it was deepest, he called, "Come on. Feel every step. Make sure you get a handhold."

Roberta and Ernst started working their way forward. As Roberta reached the first of the branches thrown in by Fritz, she gave him a grateful look. But then, glimpsing something else, she gave a bloodcurdling scream.

A giant anaconda snake was slithering through the water toward them. Ernst, trying to get away with Roberta, slipped and fell, pulling her down. At this moment, Fritz, on shore, seized his kris and moved out toward the huge snake.

"Hurry up! Get across!" he shouted.

Scrambling up onto firm ground, they turned back to see a blurred mass of action. Boy and giant snake were locked in combat, Fritz lashing wildly with his kris, and the anaconda churning up the water with its tail.

Roberta screamed. "Ernst, do something!"

Just then the snake glided off and Fritz stumbled to shore.

Ernst was almost in tears. "What could *I* do, Fritz?" he said. "I didn't even have a knife! The pistol was wet! If I'd just had something!"

"It's all right," Fritz said sharply. *"It's all right."*

Roberta was huddled on the ground, with her face buried in her hands. Dropping to his knees beside her, Fritz said, "It's all right now."

"I can't go on, Fritz," she sobbed. "I just can't."

"Sure you can," said Fritz. "I think the worst is over."

Just then they heard a low moan and, turning, they saw Ernst scrabbling at his chest, feeling for something that wasn't there.

"Oh . . . no!" Ernst moaned. "The compass . . . it's gone! I lost it out in the swamp!"

CHRISTMAS IN THE TREE HOUSE

It was almost two weeks later.

The tree house was decorated for Christmas. Under a small tree were several unopened packages, bound with leaves and improvised trimmings.

The mother was sitting before her Christmas present—the small organ that had been fastened to the wall of Captain Willhelm's cabin. The organ wheezed slightly and several of its keys stuck, but the mother beamed with gratitude.

She shook her head in wonder. "I still don't see how you managed to get it ashore."

"Fritz and Ernst helped before they left," said the father. "It was going to be . . . well . . . it's from all of us."

At this, the mother grew pale. Moving hastily to change the subject, the father stooped to kiss the back of her neck. "Merry Christmas, my dear," he said.

Just then Francis looked up from his Christmas present, a small-size crossbow. "Are we ever going to open the other presents?" he asked.

The mother braced herself. "Those," she said, "are for Fritz and Ernst."

"I know," Francis said impatiently. "But suppose they don't come back? Suppose they get ate up?"

Glaring, the father said, "Francis, it's past your bedtime."

Francis picked up his crossbow like a martyr, and started shuffling off. The mother sat at the organ, her eyes staring straight ahead.

"Play something," the father said gently. "Play *Tannenbaum*."

With supreme effort, the mother forced herself to play a few bars of the song. At this moment, a deep-throated growl came from the two dogs. Cocking their ears, they moved toward the stairway.

What could they have heard? Straining, the father listened, and for a brief moment thought he heard, very faintly, voices singing *Tannenbaum.* He frowned. Impossible!

The mother raised her head. And she, too, thought she heard the sound of distant music.

Together, like two sleepwalkers, the father and the mother moved slowly to the railing. There, they waited breathlessly . . . until at last they saw Fritz and Ernst stagger into sight. With their sons came a young zebra carrying a small figure swathed in a blanket.

"Merry Christmas, everybody!" Ernst cried hoarsely.

Francis bolted down the stairs. "Where have you been?" he cried. "We thought you were dead or something."

Before Fritz and Ernst could answer, Francis flashed by them. He had eyes only for the zebra—a new pet . . . !

An hour later, Fritz and Ernst, bathed and wearing new home-tailored shirts, were seated in the main room with the father and Francis.

"It's a great thing you boys have done," said the father.

"Fritz did most of it," said Ernst. "After I lost the compass, we were all ready to give up, but he wouldn't let us. And just when Roberta couldn't walk another step, Fritz caught the zebra . . ."

The father said thoughtfully, "Whoever did it, we must make sure it's not wasted. Now the pirates know you took their prisoner . . . they know you're somewhere on the island. They won't just forget that."

Francis jumped up. "Will the pirates come here? I'll shoot them with my crossbow. Whiz! Whiz! Whiz!"

The father sighed. "I'm afraid it'll take more than a crossbow."

"The cannon!" Ernst said eagerly. "We can bring in the cannon from the ship."

The father shook his head. "It's too corroded." Then, after a pause, "First thing tomorrow we'd better go out to the ship; take everything off, and then blow it up. We can't take any chances of it serving as a beacon for the pirates."

"What good would that do?" said Fritz. "The pirates already know it's there."

"I'm hoping," the father said slowly, "with hundreds of islands, they won't remember exactly where it was."

At this moment, the mother opened the door of her room. And Roberta, wearing the mother's finest dress and looking very feminine, moved down the short winding stairs.

As Roberta entered the room, Fritz and Ernst both got the same idea. Springing up, they both held her chair for her.

A few moments later, the father said, "Since it's such a happy occasion, why not a little dance?"

The mother began to play the organ; and the father bowed to Roberta. They began to dance.

Fritz's turn came next. As Fritz whirled about the floor with Roberta in his arms, the father moved over to the organ. Winking broadly at his wife, he said, "Haven't I told you? Anything you really need, this island will produce it. Even a girl."

With a twinkle, the mother said as she continued playing, "A girl . . . but we have three sons."

Just then, glancing across the room, the father saw Ernst move grimly forward to tap Fritz on the shoulder. Reluctantly, Fritz backed away. And as Ernst whirled off with Roberta, Fritz was glaring after them.

"Life may become very complicated," the mother whispered. "Perhaps I should have given Roberta a *simpler* dress."

READY TO FIGHT

The next morning, a dull boom thundered across the waters.

And out on the reef, the ship exploded, sending masts, spars, and timbers hurtling through the air.

Later, everyone went to a rocky area on the top of the hill overlooking the lagoon. The father stood like a general addressing his troops.

"If the pirates come," he said, "we'll be outnumbered ten to one. Up here—if we prepare in advance—we may hold out for some time."

Pointing down the hill, the father continued.

"There's where they'll try to come up. So down there we'll put . . . anything we can think of to slow them down."

Francis raised his hand. "We could dig some pits, and put lions and tigers in them—and then the pirates will come along and fall in!"

The father smiled wryly. "You do that," he said. "You're in charge of the tigers, Francis."

And so, with the same infinite care and patience with which they had built their tree house, the Swiss family started preparing for the pirate attack. Everybody worked from the crack of dawn until long past sundown. And bit by bit, thinking of something new every day, they installed fortifications which must have been without parallel in military history.

But they were racing against time. There was always the fear that the pirates might arrive before they could finish. Under so much pressure, it was only natural that

nerves should rub raw and tempers grow short. Ernst and Fritz, however, seemed to feel the strain more than any of the others.

The father had devised a way of making bombs by pouring gunpowder and gravel into coconut shells and adding a fuse sealed with melted wax. One day, while making some of these coconut bombs with Roberta, Ernst said grandly:

"I'd like to *be* something in the world . . . that's why I want to go to school."

"Oh, and you'd love it in London where I live!" said Roberta. "There are parties and dances . . . ladies in beautiful gowns . . . men in tall hats." She paused, eyeing him. "Did you ever own a tall hat, Ernst?"

As Ernst blushed, Roberta went on, laughing gaily. "I can't wait to see you in one! You'll be absolutely handsome."

His head down, Ernst stammered, "I know I'll like it especially . . . London, I mean . . . if *you're* there."

Just then Francis wandered by. Stopping, he picked up a bomb and examined it curiously.

"Francis! Don't!" Roberta cried out in alarm. "If you dropped it . . . it could blow us all to pieces!"

Ernst laughed. "Just dropping it wouldn't set it off. You have to light the fuse. Even then, I'm not so sure."

Roberta's eyes widened. "You don't think they'll work?"

"Oh, they may make a *noise*," said Ernst. "That's about all they're good for."

Francis glared. "Just because Papa thought up the coconut bombs instead of you!" he shouted.

Roberta quickly tried to change the subject. "What about your tiger?" she asked Francis. "Have you caught him yet?"

Francis spread his hands resignedly. "No, because until Fritz and Ernst get the pits dug . . . I wouldn't have any place to keep my old tiger."

At this moment, Fritz called from where he was working on a huge log pile at the brink of the hill. "One of you . . . Roberta . . . come over here a minute, will you?"

Ernst made a face. "I'll go," he said.

But Roberta had already rushed off eagerly.

Scowling with annoyance, Ernst turned back to making bombs. But now his hands moved listlessly and his eyes wandered. With every dragging moment, his scowl deepened. And suddenly he turned and stalked toward the brink of the hill.

Meanwhile, Francis had wandered back to the bombs. Stealthily picking one up, he took a candle and lit the fuse. As the fuse started to sputter, he looked around for a place to throw the bomb.

The bomb had hardly left his fingers before it exploded violently!

The father and mother were laying fuses in shallow trenches that led down the hillside to a mined area. Hearing the explosion, the father shouted, "Pirates! Positions, everybody!"

Hurrying over from the log pile, Fritz, Ernst, and Roberta met the father and mother rushing up the hill.

"Francis!" cried the mother. "Where is he?"

Beaming with pride and excitement, Francis scrambled toward them. "Those coconut bombs," he said. "You don't have to worry. They work *real* good!"

The mother rushed forward to seize him. "You might have been killed!" she sobbed.

Whirling upon Ernst, Fritz said angrily, "If you'd stayed by the bombs, like you were *supposed* to, this wouldn't have happened."

Ernst tightened his jaw. "Don't you tell *me* what I'm supposed to do!"

"Quiet, both of you!" the father said sharply. "That's enough! This incident is over, and I don't want to hear another word about it from either of you."

But a few days later, Fritz and Roberta were working together again. He was booby-trapping a small bridge near the bottom of the hill. And she was seated on the bank beside him.

"If you don't want to go to school . . ." Roberta was saying, "if your mind's made up . . . maybe my grandfather could give you a job. It would be a *good* job, Fritz."

Fritz looked troubled. "It's not that I don't appreciate it," he said, "but . . . well . . . that's just not for me . . . cooped up in an office day after day."

Pouting, Roberta asked, "What *would* you like to do?"

"I'd like to do what we started *out* to do . . . go on to New Guinea . . . be part of the new colony . . ."

"Oh," Roberta said flatly.

Then, watching him out of the corner of her eye, she said, "Ernst was very flattering. He told me he'd like to be in London if *I* were there."

Just then Ernst emerged beaming from the jungle. On his head was a tall hat woven from coconut fronds. Tipping the hat and bowing from the waist, he said to Roberta, "May I have the next dance, m'lady?"

Roberta curtsied, laughing with delight. Ernst held up the hat for her to admire. "A touch of London in the jungle," he said. "I thought maybe I could make you feel at home."

Fritz glowered. "I thought you were supposed to be covering the pits," he said.

Turning abruptly, Ernst said, "And I thought *you* were supposed to be working on the bridges."

Suddenly they all heard Francis calling, "Fritz, come here. I want to show you something . . ."

Fritz and Roberta moved toward the beach, and Ernst followed angrily. Francis had set up a crude "A" frame over a pit camouflaged with palm fronds. Francis pointed triumphantly to a piece of meat dangling from the frame.

"The old tiger will come along at night, and he'll smell the meat, and jump for it, and that's how I'll catch my tiger."

Ernst said with a sneer, "You think a tiger's going to fall for something like that? You're wasting your time."

"*You* talk about wasting time?" Fritz said. "How many hours did you spend on that silly hat?"

"None of your business," screamed Ernst. "You're not my boss! *I'll show you . . . !*"

With these words, Ernst threw a wild punch. Blocking the blow easily, Fritz sent him staggering with a push.

As Ernst barrelled in again with flailing fists, Francis shouted jubilantly, "Fight! Fight! Fight!"

The father came rushing down the hill. "What's this all about?" he wanted to know. "What is this? What started it?"

"Nothing," Fritz said dully; and Ernst shrugged and looked away.

The father frowned thoughtfully as he stared at his two sons. "Maybe I've been pushing you too hard," he said. "We're all on edge . . . working day and night. Tomorrow we're going to relax . . . and observe the first national holiday in New Switzerland."

"Yippee!" Francis shouted. "A holiday!"

After finishing the day's work, they started getting ready for the holiday. All evening they cut banners and strung them up. The sky grew dark and the stars came out. And then they wove garlands of flowers.

Suddenly from the pit area came the sound of breaking palm fronds. And then they heard some huge beast thrashing about in the dark, growling and hissing viciously.

Bounding down the tree house steps, Francis shouted at the top of his lungs:

"Mama! You don't have to worry any more! I got my tiger!"

INTERRUPTED HOLIDAY

The holiday dawned warm and cloudless. Flags and bunting hung everywhere; and all morning there were games, dances, and then a special holiday picnic. By the time the afternoon came, everybody was smiling.

"Ladies and gentlemen," called the father, "now for the main event of the day . . . *the assorted animal race! The winner will win a delicious cake . . . which all of us will eat!*"

A titter of laughter rose from the starting line where the jockeys were getting their strange mounts ready.

Francis was clambering up on the elephant. Ernst was busy adjusting a bridle on an ostrich. Roberta was already aboard the zebra and Fritz was mounted on the donkey.

And Francis's monkey, dressed up for the holiday, was mounted on Duke's back, chattering and hissing excitedly.

Bowing, the father handed a pistol to the mother. "This lovely lady will serve as the official starter," he said.

Squinting and bracing herself, the mother held the pistol up. As she squeezed the trigger, the contestants were off and running—in all directions!

For a short time, the ostrich and the zebra were in the lead, racing neck to neck. But suddenly the zebra, with Roberta barely hanging on, decided to climb the hill.

And then the ostrich, too, decided to blaze a trail of its own. It collided with the donkey and the elephant, who had wandered off to the stream. The zebra skidded down the hill in a cloud of dust to join the mix-up. And then Duke, barking excitedly, started running figure-eights around the legs of the other animals. By now, everybody—jockeys as well as spectators—was doubled up with laughter.

The snorting, wild-eyed zebra was the first to fight its way clear of the tangle. Leaving the course, the zebra bolted onto the beach. There, it turned abruptly, flopping Roberta off onto the sand.

Roberta was still laughing as she rose to her feet. But then, glancing up, she saw a ship anchored out beyond the reefs—and several longboats pulling toward the island.

She froze. The pirates!

They must have been cruising nearby. They had heard the pistol shot at the start of the race—and now they were coming to get her back.

Roberta plunged into the jungle. When the father saw her white face, he asked, "What is it? What's the matter?"

"Pirates!" she whispered. "Right here on our beach!"

The father set his jaw. Then, like a general leading his troops into battle, he said grimly, "All right, everybody! Right now! Up on the hill with you!"

THE BATTLE ON THE HILL

Kuala and his pirates swarmed ashore from their longboats. Swinging their kris and shouting angrily, they made their way to the small bridge near the bottom of the hill.

From behind a thick bush midway up the hill, Fritz and Ernst watched the pirates start across the bridge. Suddenly the brothers yanked on a rope with all their strength.

The tightened rope pulled the main support out from under the bridge. And as the decking went crashing down, at least a dozen pirates plunged into the water, yelling in fear.

Now the two brothers gave a mighty tug on another rope. This one tripped several crossbows, sending a rain of arrows flying down to plague the pirates thrashing in the water.

Fritz and Ernst were grinning broadly as they rushed to join the others in the dugout at the top of the hill. There, peering down over the dugout's parapet, they all watched Kuala rally his men and urge them onward. One by one, moving slowly and cautiously, the pirates started up the hillside.

Suddenly one of them screamed. He had been thrown back by a sprung tree branch and hurled bodily into a nest of cactus. A

moment later, another pirate stepped into a snare trap. A bent-over tree sprung up, whipping him into the air.

But the pirates, whipped on by Kuala's shouts, continued climbing. And when several moments went by without their encountering any more traps, they seemed to take heart. Brandishing their knives and cheering, they charged up the hill.

The pirates' fierceness cooled slightly when two of them were abruptly swallowed up by the earth. It cooled some more when they heard a horrendous growling coming from the spot where their henchmen had disappeared.

Up in the dugout, Frances screamed with delight, "He got them! My tiger got them!"

Suddenly, defying all laws of gravity, the two pirates shot out of the pit, their clothes in ribbons. Down the hill they ran; and although Kuala shouted, screamed, and even took some pistol shots at them, the two deserters never stopped until they reached the longboats.

A few minutes later, Ernst reported from the parapet:

"Kuala's rallied them again . . . they'll be over the mines soon . . . area three."

Grinning, the father moved over to where several numbered fuses came together. He applied a burning torch to the proper one; and the fuse started to sputter. Flames moved rapidly along it, over the edge of the parapet.

A trail of smoke hurried down the hillside, and suddenly the ground under the pirates erupted with explosions. Rising dazedly, the pirates moved in a body to take refuge behind a nearby pile of rocks.

The father touched off another fuse. Again a trail of smoke hurried down the hillside— and this time the rock pile exploded.

But still the pirates came on. With coconut bombs bursting all about him, Kuala now ordered a frontal attack.

With a mighty swing of his axe, the father cut the heavy rope looped around the huge log pile at the brink of the hill. The logs went crashing down, sweeping the pirates before them.

After this, there was a brief lull. Then one of Kuala's henchmen tied a white shirt to his kris and waved it in truce.

"Kuala make talk; you hear?" called Kuala.

"We hear you!" the father answered grimly.

"Give back boy — no more fight. You hear?"

"You want the 'boy,' you come and get him," the father answered. "We're ready for you."

The pirate chief made one last call. "You make Kuala fight long time, he win! Then you *die* . . . and Kuala will take boy."

Up in the dugout, Roberta said, "It's true. We can't possibly stand them off forever."

"They're coming up there! I hear them!" yelled Francis.

The treacherous Kuala had used the truce to send some of his men in a flanking movement around the back of the dugout. And the first pirate was already surging up over the parapet.

The father sent him hurtling into space with a hard push. But then another pirate leaped at the father from behind.

Whirling, Fritz quickly fired the loaded musket thrust into his hands by Roberta; and the father was free to tangle with a third pirate.

Now Francis, who had edged partway down the sloping side of the hill, whistled piercingly and shouted:

"Here, Turk! Here, Duke! Here, boys!"

"Francis! Look out!" the mother screamed.

Just in time, Francis leaped aside as a pirate made a grab at him. As the pirate chased Francis up toward the dugout, the mother scrambled out to help.

Whirling to a stop, Francis saw the pirate seize his mother.

Wild with anger, he picked up a rock and hurled it. The rock scored a perfect bullseye, right in the middle of the pirate's forehead; and losing his grip on the mother, the pirate staggered off.

Just then Duke and Turk came bounding up, and Francis bent to hug them. But then, glancing toward the dugout, he saw Kuala creeping over the parapet in front.

Motioning, Francis cried, "Go get him, Duke! Go, Turk!"

The pirate chief fired his pistol, wounding the father. As the father went down, Kuala leaped into the dugout and grappled with Fritz and Ernst.

Just then Duke and Turk came hurtling through the air and struck Kuala full in the chest, driving him back to the parapet. For a moment he teetered on the edge, and then he tumbled down the bluff.

In the dugout, the wounded father grimaced with pain. "They'll try again," he gasped. "But we've still got a chance. Make every shot count."

The others nodded, but they looked troubled. And then, suddenly, they all heard the boom of a distant cannon.

Fritz shuddered. In a voice heavy with despair, he announced: "Now they're shelling us from the ship!"

ON THE BEACH

More cannons boomed. Then they heard excited Malaysian shouting, followed by the sound of running feet.

Peering cautiously over the parapet, Fritz saw the pirates scrambling down the bluff and rushing to the longboats.

"Ernst," said the father, puzzled, "hand me the telescope . . ."

Squinting through the glass, the father cried excitedly, "A ship! A merchantman! It's firing on the pirates!"

Roberta stood up, and all at once a radiant smile lit up her face. "It's one of my grandfather's ships!" she cried joyously, throwing both arms about Fritz. "Oh, I told you he would come!"

Just then the anchored pirate junk took a hit in the powder magazine. With a terrific boom, it blew completely apart.

Later, when Roberta's grandfather came ashore in a longboat, he told them:

"We were heading up the coast, stopping at every likely spot. We heard the shooting. It's a good thing we did!"

And then he insisted that the Swiss family let him show his gratitude. He was very wealthy—and almost anything at all that they might wish for, he could do for them—

It was the next day now, and the mother was serving tea in the main room of the tree house. All were dressed in their best clothes, and luggage was piled about.

Ernst sat staring straight ahead of him, almost in a trance. "Roberta and I talked about going to school," he said dazedly, "but the *university* . . . I never dreamed . . ."

The old captain smiled. "Nothing to it," he said. "I've been making donations to them for years. About time I asked for something."

Then, turning to the father and the mother, he said, "As for the rest of you, if you'd like to return to Europe, I think I could make it interesting for you . . . give you a fresh start."

The father looked unhappy, but he didn't say anything.

"If you still want to go to New Guinea, I'll be happy to take you there," the captain said.

At this, the father looked to his wife. Moving behind his chair and placing her hand on his shoulder, she said quietly, "I think my husband and I would rather just stay here . . ."

Amazed and delighted, the father rose slowly. "Are you sure it's what *you* want?" he asked.

The mother nodded. "It's been a good life here, for us."

Then, as the father hugged her in a wildly joyous embrace, she said, "Fritz and Ernst will go, but for a few years we'll keep Francis here with us."

"You won't remain without neighbors for long; you realize that?" said the captain. "It's a new island; there'll be a new colony . . . a new Governor."

Beaming at the father, Ernst said proudly, "They'll likely make *you* the Governor."

The captain nodded. "*More* than likely, I would say . . ."

Roberta left the tree house and walked slowly and thoughtfully toward the pond. Fritz was sitting there on the bank, moodily tossing pebbles into the water.

Standing over him, Roberta said, "Funny, isn't it . . . how you can change your mind about what's important? . . . what it is you really want . . ."

As Fritz glanced up curiously, Roberta went on. "I mean . . . like your parents. All the time they've been working to get to New Guinea . . . and now when they have the chance, they realize that everything they want is right here . . ."

"You mean they're *not* going?" gasped Fritz.

"No," said Roberta, "they're not. And I think I can understand how they feel."

Nodding gravely, Fritz said, "I do, too." Then, reaching for her hand, he said, "If two people have each other, and they're on an island like this, what more could they want?"

As Fritz raised her hand to his lips, Roberta said, "Just to be alone, I guess."

Just then Ernst came, calling, "Roberta? Fritz? We have to leave now. The captain wants to go with the tide . . ."

"We'll be right there," said Roberta. Then, smiling impishly at Fritz, she added, "Just to say good-bye. And I'll have to *explain* to my grandfather . . ."

And so Ernst was the only one to leave in the longboat with Roberta's grandfather. As the longboat dwindled slowly in the distance, the father, the mother, Fritz, Roberta, and Francis stood on the beach waving good-bye. And long after the merchantman had pulled anchor and sailed away, they stood on in silence and looked out over the sea.

Suddenly the mother stirred uneasily. She had a strange feeling that something was missing on this wonderful island where everything you needed was always right at your fingertips. Then glancing about the beach, she saw that it was *someone*, rather than something . . .

You see, Francis had wandered off again.

BAMBI

BAMBI came into the world in the middle of a forest thicket. The little, hidden thicket was scarcely big enough for the new baby and his mother.

But the magpie soon spied him there.

"What a beautiful baby!" she cried. And away she flew to spread the news to all the other animals of the forest.

Her chattering soon brought dozens of birds and animals to the thicket. The rabbits came hurrying; the squirrels came a-scurrying. The robins and bluebirds fluttered and flew.

At last even the old owl woke up from his long day's sleep.

"Who, who?" the owl said sleepily, hearing all the commotion.

"Wake up, Friend Owl!" a rabbit called. "It's happened! The young Prince is born!"

"Everyone's going to see him," said the squirrels. "You come, too."

With a sigh the owl spread his wings and flew off toward the thicket. There he found squirrels and rabbits and birds peering through the bushes at a doe and a little spotted fawn.

The fawn was Bambi, the new Prince of the Forest.

"Congratulations," said the owl, speaking for all the animals. "This is quite an occasion. It isn't often that a Prince is born in the forest."

The doe looked up. "Thank you," she said quietly. Then with her nose she gently nudged her sleeping baby until he lifted his head and looked around.

She nudged him again, and licked him reassuringly. At last he pushed up on his thin legs, trying to stand.

"Look! He's trying to stand up already!" shouted one of the little rabbits, Thumper by name. "He's wobbly, though, isn't he?"

"Thumper!" the mother rabbit exclaimed, "that's not a pleasant thing to say!"

The new fawn's legs were not very steady, it was true, but at last he stood beside his mother. Now all the animals could see the fine white spots on his red-brown coat, and the sleepy expression on his soft baby face.

The forest around him echoed with countless small voices. A soft breeze rustled the leaves about the thicket. And the watching animals whispered among themselves. But the little fawn did not listen to any of them. He only knew that his mother's tongue was licking him softly, washing and warming him. He nestled closer to her, and closed his eyes.

Quietly the animals and birds slipped away through the forest.

Thumper the rabbit was the last to go.

"What are you going to name the young Prince?" he asked.

"I'll call him Bambi," the mother answered.

"Bambi," Thumper repeated. "Bambi. That's a good name. Good-bye, Bambi." And he hopped away after his sisters.

Bambi was not a sleepy baby for long. Soon he was following his mother down the narrow forest paths. Bright flowers winked from beneath the leaves.

Squirrels and chipmunks looked up and called, "Good morning, young Prince."

Opossums, hanging by their long tails from a tree branch, said, "Hello, Prince Bambi."

The fawn looked at them all with wondering eyes. But he did not say a word.

Finally, as Bambi and his mother reached a little clearing in the forest, they met Thumper and his family.

"Hi, Bambi," said Thumper. "Let's play."

"Yes, let's play," Thumper's sister cried. And away they hopped, over branches and hillocks and tufts of grass.

Bambi soon understood the game, and he began to jump and run on his stiff, spindly legs.

Thumper jumped over a log and his sisters followed.

"Come on, Bambi," Thumper called. "Hop over the log."

Bambi jumped, but not far enough. He fell with a plop on top of the log.

"Too bad," said Thumper. "You'll do better next time."

Bambi untangled his legs and stood up again. But still he did not speak. He pranced along behind Thumper, and soon he saw a family of birds sitting on a branch.

Bambi looked at them.

"Those are birds, Bambi," Thumper told him. "Birds."

"Bir-d," Bambi said slowly. The young Prince had spoken his first word!

Thumper and his sisters were all excited, and Bambi himself was pleased. He repeated the word over and over to himself. Then he saw a butterfly cross the path. "Bird, bird!" he cried again.

"No, Bambi," said Thumper. "That's not a bird. That's a butterfly."

The butterfly disappeared into a clump of yellow flowers. Bambi bounded toward them happily.

"Butterfly!" he cried.

"No, Bambi," said Thumper. "Not butterfly. *Flower.*"

He pushed his nose into the flowers and sniffed. Bambi did the same, but suddenly he drew back. His nose had touched something warm and furry.

Out from the bed of flowers came a small black head with two shining eyes.

"Flower!" said Bambi.

The black eyes twinkled. As the little animal stepped out, the white stripe down his black furry back glistened in the sun.

Thumper the rabbit was laughing so hard that he could scarcely speak.

"That's not a flower," said Thumper. "That's a skunk."

"Flower," repeated Bambi.

"I don't care," said the skunk. "The young Prince can call me Flower if he wants to. I don't mind."

So Flower, the skunk, got his name.

One morning Bambi and his mother walked down a new path. It grew lighter and lighter as they walked along. Soon the trail ended in a tangle of bushes and vines, and Bambi could see a great, bright, open space spread out before them.

Bambi wanted to bound out there to play in the sunshine, but his mother stopped him. "Wait," she said. "You must never run out on the meadow without making sure it is safe."

She took a few slow, careful steps forward. She listened and sniffed in all directions. Then she called, "Come."

Bambi bounded out. He felt so good and so happy that he leaped into the air again and again. For the meadow was the most beautiful place he had ever seen.

His mother dashed forward and showed him how to race and play in the tall grass.

Bambi ran after her. He felt as if he were flying. Round and round they raced in great circles. At last his mother stopped and stood still, catching her breath.

Then Bambi set out by himself to explore the meadow. Soon he spied his little friend the skunk, sitting in the shade of some blossoms.

"Good morning, Flower," said Bambi.

And he found Thumper and his sisters nibbling sweet clover.

"Try some, Bambi," said Thumper.

So Bambi did.

Suddenly a big green frog popped out of the clover patch and hopped over to a meadow pond. Bambi had not seen the pond before, so he hurried over for a closer look.

As the fawn came near, the frog hopped into the water.

Where could he have gone? Bambi wondered. So he bent down to look into the pond. As the ripples cleared, Bambi jumped back. For he saw a fawn down there in the water, looking out at him!

"Don't be frightened, Bambi," his mother told him. "You are just seeing yourself in the water."

So Bambi looked once more. This time he saw *two* fawns looking back at him! He jumped back again, and as he lifted his head he saw that it was true—there was another little fawn standing beside him!

"Hello," she said.

Bambi backed away and ran to his mother, where she was quietly eating grass beside another doe. Bambi leaned against her and peered out at the other little fawn, who had followed him.

"Don't be afraid, Bambi," his mother said. "This is little Faline, and this is your Aunt Ena. Can't you say hello to them?"

"Hello, Bambi," said the two deer. But Bambi did not say a word.

"You have been wanting to meet other deer," his mother reminded him. "Well, Aunt Ena and Faline are deer like us. Now can't you speak to them?"

"Hello," whispered Bambi in a small, small voice.

"Come and play, Bambi," said Faline. She leaned forward and licked his face.

Bambi dashed away as fast as he could run, and Faline raced after him. They almost flew over that meadow.

Up and down they chased each other. Over the little hillocks they raced.

When they stopped, all topsy-turvy and breathless, they were good friends.

Then they walked side by side on the bright meadow, visiting quietly together.

One morning, Bambi woke up shivering with cold. Even before he opened his eyes, his nose told him there was something new and strange in the world. Then he looked out of the thicket. Everything was covered with white.

"It is snow, Bambi," his mother said. "Go ahead and walk out. It is all right."

Bambi stepped out onto the snow very cautiously. His feet sank deep into the soft blanket. He had to lift them up high as he walked along. Now and then, with a soft

plop, a tiny snowy heap would tumble from a leaf overhead onto his nose or back.

Bambi was delighted. The sun glittered so brightly on the whiteness. The air was so mild and clear. And all around him white snow stars came whirling down.

From the crest of a little hill he saw Thumper. Thumper was sitting on the top of the pond!

"Come on, Bambi!" Thumper shouted. "Look! The water's stiff!" He thumped with one foot against the solid ice. "You can even slide on it. Watch and I'll show you how!"

Thumper took a run and slid swiftly across the pond. Bambi tried it, too, but his legs shot out from under him and down he crashed on the hard ice. That was not so much fun.

"Let's play something else," Bambi suggested, when he had carefully pulled himself to his feet again. "Where's Flower?"

"I think I know," said Thumper.

He led Bambi to the doorway of a deep burrow. They peered down into it. There, peacefully sleeping on a bed of withered flowers, lay the little skunk.

"Wake up, Flower!" Bambi called.

"Is it spring yet?" Flower asked sleepily, half opening his eyes.

"No, winter's just beginning," Bambi said. "What are you doing?"

"Hibernating," the little skunk replied. "Flowers always sleep in the winter, you know."

Thumper yawned. "I guess I'll take a nap, too," he said. "Good-bye, Bambi. I'll see you later."

So Bambi wandered back to the thicket.

"Don't fret, Bambi," his mother said. "Winter will soon be over, and spring will come again."

So Bambi went to sleep beside his mother in the snug, warm thicket, and dreamed of the jolly games that he and his friends would play in the wonderful spring to come.

DARBY O'GILL

Now IRELAND, as you may know, is a green and lovely land. There's many a thousand of Irishmen there, in every valley and town.

But there are others in Ireland, too, who make their homes snug underground. You may not see one of them from New Year's Eve to year's end. But they are there, make no mistake. They're the Little People, the leprechauns.

A canny lot of wee folk are they, dressed in their suits of green. And many's the crock of gold they have miserly hidden away. But will they share it with human folk? They'll give you a trick instead!

Take the case of Darby O'Gill, which happened not long ago:

Darby was chasing his horse one night. The skittish mare led him across the sloping meadow and off toward the mountain beyond.

Now Darby knew as well as the next what dangers that mountain held. For it had the name of Knocknasheega, the hill that belonged to the fairy folk.

And sure enough, elfin music seemed to rise up from the place. Darby heard it plain enough. It came from an open well. And a strange sort of light seemed to rise from there too.

Well, Darby was a man with his share of wonder. He bent down to peek down the hole.

As he did so, the fairy music grew wilder. Darby heard his horse give one strange, wild neigh. Then he felt her hooves upon his shoulders. And he tumbled down that well!

When he came to himself, he was flat on his back, lying on the floor of a cave.

Suddenly, spang, a wee man landed on Darby's middle!

Darby waved his stick.

"You wicked little creatures!" he cried.

"Watch your stick!" cried one of the leprechauns. And Darby's own trusty black-thorn flew out of his hands and beat its master's head!

"Come on," said the other leprechaun. "We'll take you to our king."

Darby had nothing better to do, so he followed the little men. Many were the wonderful sights he saw, in those caves deep underground. He saw leprechauns shoveling crocks full of gold. He saw others cobbling small fairy shoes.

"Well, Darby O'Gill!" cried the Little People's king, laying aside his pipes. "I'm pleased and delighted to see you!"

"Thank you sir," Darby said.

"Sit down," said the king, and waved his hand at a chest by the foot of his throne.

"Drop the lid, man," he said, as Darby just stared. "It's only an old chest of jewels."

Darby closed the lid and sat down.

Then Brian the king showed him the treasures here and there, scattered about the room.

"I declare to my soul!" cried Darby O'Gill. "When I tell this at home, they'll never believe me."

"Oh, you'll not do that, Darby," said the king with a smile. "Once you're here, there's no going back, you know."

"But I've got to go back!" cried Darby.

"Ah, no," said the little king. "You can say good-bye to the tears and the troubles of the world outside. There's nothing but fun and dancing here. Be a good lad now and give us a tune."

"Well," said Darby, with a glint in his eye, "I'm no great hand with the pipes or harp. But give me my old fiddle, and I can play you a tune worth going a mile o'ground to hear."

"Grand, grand," said Brian the King.

"But I'll have to go home," said Darby O'Gill. "To get the fiddle, you see."

"None of your tricks," said King Brian sternly. "I said you were here to stay."

He gave a snap of his fingers, and a fine old fiddle and its bow dropped into Darby's hands.

"Go ahead," said King Brian. "Give us a good one."

Darby tucked the fiddle under his chin and tried a chord or two. They sounded so magnificent that a bold plan came to him.

"I'll play you the Fox Chase," said Darby O'Gill. For he knew that the Little People loved both the dance and the hunt. They could not resist them at all.

Well, he played the gathering of the huntsmen and the hounds, and the start of the hunt.

"Off we go!" cried Darby, tapping his foot.

And the little men started to dance.

He played them the long, lone sound of the horn and the fine, fast music of the chase. You could hear the hounds baying and the riders galloping.

Soon the Little People were racing off to mount their white hunters. With the king at their head, they circled the cave, while Darby fiddled the baying of a hound.

"Tally ho!" cried the king, with a crack of his whip. And the mountainside opened before him.

Then the moonlight flooded in, dazzling Darby's eyes. But he kept on fiddling as never before. And out streamed the king, with his hunters behind him, toward the night sky filled with the glory of all the stars above.

When Darby was alone in the cave, he laid down the fiddle and started after them. But of a sudden he thought of the chest of jewels beside the throne.

Back he went and he lifted the lid and began to stuff his pockets with jewels.

A strange grating sound made him turn his head. The mountainside was closing again! Darby reached for one last handful of jewels. But he saw there was not a moment to lose! So he raced for the opening, narrowed now to a crack in the mountainside.

Out he dove headlong. And as he sprawled in the night-chilled grass, with a crash the mountain behind him closed. He shuddered at his narrow escape!

Then his hand went to his jewel-crammed pocket. Not a thing was there. Deeper he dug. Still only cloth. And then, at the bottom, he found a hole. As he had fled from the cave, all the jewels had trickled out!

So that was how it came about that Darby O'Gill came back to his home from a night with the Little People, with not a glint of a treasure to show.

There were even those who doubted his word. But you and I understand.

BIG RED

Big Red was a beautiful Red Setter.

He was not a house dog or a pet dog.

He was a show dog and lived in the kennels of a very rich man.

His master looked after him carefully, because he wanted Big Red to win first prize in shows.

Every day Big Red was brushed and combed.

He had lots to eat and went for walks every day.

But Big Red was unhappy, because he did not have a friend to play with.

He did not *belong* to anybody.

Then one day a boy came to the kennels.

His name was René.

And he and Big Red became friends.

Now René brushed Big Red's fine coat.

René fed Big Red and took him for walks.

René and Big Red played games together.

They played at walking-along-a-log.

They played jumping-across-the-stream.

They played chasing-around-the-tree.

And in the evenings, they sat quietly together while René played a song on his harmonica.

René and Big Red were friends.

But Big Red was still a show dog.

And one day his master said, "Big Red, you are not a house dog. You are not a pet dog. You are a show dog. And tomorrow you must go to the big city."

Sadly, Big Red sat in his cage in the train.

The kind guard let Big Red out of his cage.

"There you are, boy, stretch those fine long legs," said the guard. "I'll get you some water."

Suddenly the train went around a curve. The doors of Big Red's car slid open.

And Big Red jumped out.

"That is the end of Big Red," said his master when he heard the news. "Big Red does not know how to hunt. He is a show dog. He cannot live in the wild woods."

"I will find him. I must find him," said René.

"You will never find him," said the master. "The woods are big and wild. And you, too, will get lost."

"My uncle taught me many things about the woods," said René. "I will go there and look for Big Red."

René got on the train—the same train that had carried Big Red.

"You will never find him, son," said the same kind guard.

Suddenly the train went around a curve, and René saw that the train slowed down.

"Perhaps *this* is where he jumped off," said René. And René jumped off, too.

René wondered which way to go. Then he saw a stream.

"Perhaps Big Red drank some water here," he thought.

René walked along the bank. And sure enough, there was a footprint!

"It's a dog's footprint! It *must* be Big Red's!"

René walked and walked, but there were no more footprints. It began to grow dark.

Suddenly René stopped. His sharp eyes had seen something caught in a thistle. It was a piece of red hair—Big Red's hair!

"Big Red, Big Red!" called René.

But there was no answering bark.

Now the sun was setting. Sadly, René unrolled his blanket and lay down.

As soon as morning came, René set off again.

"Big Red, Big Red," he called.

But there was no answering bark.

René walked and walked.

He saw a clump of grass that lay flat. Perhaps Big Red had slept there.

"Big Red, Big Red!" called René.

But his voice sounded small in the tall mountains.

Tiredly, René sat down under a tree.

He pulled out his harmonica and began to play a sad little tune.

The music rose sweet and clear in the mountain air. It rose above the treetops. It drifted softly down the valley to a quiet pool.

And Big Red, drinking by the pool, lifted his head.

For a moment the dog stood still, one paw lifted, his whole body quiet and listening.

And then he gave a bark and began to run.

"Big Red, Big Red!" called René. He had heard the bark. He began running. He saw a flash of red in the bushes—it was Big Red! It *was!*

The dog leaped at René and the two rolled over, René laughing and shouting, the dog barking with joy.

"Big Red, you old clown!" gasped René. "I came to find you, and you found me!"

And then he looked more closely at the dog.

"You are thin and hungry, Big Red," he said. "Come, I must take you back to your master."

When the master saw René and the dog, he could hardly believe his eyes.

"I never thought I would see either of you again."

"He found *me*, sir," said René quietly.

"Then he is yours, René," said the master. "He loves you and you love him. You belong together."

And so at last Big Red was not just a show dog.

At last he really belonged to somebody.

And at last Big Red was happy.

ZORRO

A SON COMES HOME

"MAKE WAY! Make way for the Comandante's Lancers!"

This cry rang out along the roadway leading to Los Angeles, a sleepy town in the Spanish California of 1820.

"Make way! Make way!" The cry was repeated.

Two mounted Lancers in splendid uniforms galloped down the road at breakneck speed. They led a third horse, on which sat a white-haired man whose hands were tied behind his back.

All traffic gave way for the soldiers and their prisoner. A stagecoach, its roof piled with luggage, pulled to the side. One of the passengers, a handsome, well-dressed youth named Diego de la Vega, poked his head out to watch the horsemen speed past.

"The prisoner! Why—it's Don Ignacio Torres—my father's friend!" he exclaimed to

his companion, a dark-skinned, pleasant looking man. The second passenger looked at him, puzzled.

"Yes, my father's friend," Diego said, "and one of the important *rancheros* of the district. I don't understand that at all, Bernardo. A man like Don Ignacio being arrested. This new comandante, Capitan Monastario, must be even more of a tyrant than we've heard."

The stagecoach rolled on until the *cochero* —the driver—called down, "Don Diego! We must stop at the gates of Los Angeles for inspection by the Comandante's soldiers."

"What? Another inspection? By whose orders?" Diego asked.

"The Comandante's."

"It was never so before," Diego said.

"Ah, señor—you've been away in Spain. Things have changed these past three years. The Comandante makes his own laws. And no one dares disobey them," the *cochero* said.

"Oh, I wasn't thinking of disobeying," Diego said hastily. "After all, the law is the law, and must be upheld."

He leaned over and whispered to Bernardo, "Don't forget. They must believe I'm a timid scholar."

Bernardo nodded. "Even my own father must think that," Diego added. "And you have a part to play, too, Bernardo. You know what you must do."

Bernardo held a finger to his lips, then

cupped a hand around his ear in imitation of a deaf man.

"Good! Unfortunately, you can't speak— but you must pretend you're deaf, too. That way, you'll be the ears and eyes behind my back. People grow careless around a deaf man. They say many things they would otherwise keep silent about."

The mute's grin grew wider.

"Between us, we'll give the Comandante a hard time, eh, Bernardo?"

The coach lurched to a stop and a loud voice bellowed, "All out for inspection!"

The door was yanked open. A fat, mustached Lancer with sergeant's braid on his sleeve gave the gruff order, "Get out!"

"Why, it's Sergeant Garcia!" Diego said as he and Bernardo stepped down from the coach.

"Don Diego de la Vega! What a surprise, señor! We thought you were studying at

the University in Madrid! When did you get back?" the sergeant said.

"Today, aboard the sloop *Azurra*. I see there have been some changes, Garcia. A new comandante, and so on. But you aren't bothered by changes, eh?"

"That's right, Don Diego. I'm a soldier. I simply follow orders," the man replied.

"Yes, I understand, Sergeant. Will this inspection take long? I'm anxious to get home."

"No, señor. I personally will conduct the inspection of your luggage."

"Thank you. I'll have my bags brought down by my servant." He signaled Bernardo

with his hands and the mute scrambled atop the coach to get the baggage.

"Can he not hear?" said the sergeant.

"No, nor can he speak," said Diego. "Born that way. Still he's willing, and a fine servant. I brought him from Spain with me." Don Diego's glance wandered to the Comandante's headquarters, a long, low adobe building. The guardhouse stood near it, with armed sentries pacing outside. Farther off were the stables and barracks of the Lancers.

The sentries snapped to attention as an officer came from the guardhouse.

"Is that the comandante, Capitan Monastario?" asked Diego.

"Si, señor. He must have been questioning the prisoner—a most important man— Don Ignacio Torres." Garcia cut himself short. "Oh, señor! I forgot! You know him!"

"My father's friend, Don Ignacio, is a prisoner?" Diego asked in mock astonishment.

"Si. I'm afraid it is true," Garcia said sadly.

"Oh, dear—how upsetting! I must speak to the Comandante about this!" Diego said.

Capitan Monastario was a fierce looking

man with a military bearing. He had a full beard, and was armed with a pistol and a sabre.

Diego went to him and said, "I'd like a word with you, Capitan Monastario."

"Who are you?" the Comandante demanded.

"Don Diego de la Vega."

"Ah, Don Alejandro's son. But I thought you were in Madrid, studying at the University?"

"I've returned, Señor Comandante, because the University was not a fit place in which to study," Diego said.

"What? But a university is made for studying—"

"For some, perhaps," Diego said. "But I am a poet. I must have peaceful and calm surroundings. Those university students! Mad rowdies—all of them! Can you imagine, Capitan, they liked to duel and wrestle and fight! I found it most disturbing."

The Comandante tapped the pommel of his sabre. "Then you think the pen is mightier than the sword, do you?" he asked with contempt.

"Why, yes, Capitan. I do."

"I see. Now, Señor Poet—what is it you want?"

"Why have you arrested Don Ignacio and locked him up like a common criminal?"

"Because he is worse than the lowest thief!" Monastario said.

"But, señor, there must be some mistake. Don Ignacio is—"

"A traitor! And he'll pay for his treachery and his plotting against me!" the Comandante roared. "Is there anything more?"

"N-no, Comandante!"

"Then get on with you, Don Diego! I have no time to waste talking to poets!"

"*Adios*, Comandante," Diego said, bowing. The Comandante dismissed him with a wave of his hand. Diego went to the coach, glancing back fearfully at the Comandante.

Soon the baggage was reloaded and the coach was rolling on its way to the De la Vega *rancho*.

Capitan Monastario called Sergeant Garcia to him. "What was in Diego's baggage?" the Comandante asked.

"Clothing, Capitan, and many books—poetry, I think."

A sneer twisted Monastario's lips. "Poetry! Well—Don Alejandro may be a lion, but his son is only a harmless pussy cat!"

He threw back his head and laughed. Sergeant Garcia joined him, and their mocking laughter echoed across the Plaza.

In the stagecoach, Diego leaned against the leather seat and glanced slyly at Bernardo. "The Comandante thinks he's dealing with a frightened poet—which is just what I want him to think," Diego said.

Bernardo rocked with silent mirth. But Diego did not smile. He stared moodily out of the window. "The hardest part is still ahead. I must make my father believe I'm afraid to fight, and I must go on pretending until we win justice for our people—no matter what anyone thinks of me!"

THE MARK OF ZORRO

That evening, Diego sat in the *sala*, or grand parlor, of the De la Vega *hacienda* with his father, Don Alejandro. It was a peaceful room —but Don Alejandro paced about restlessly.

"I do not understand, Diego," he said. "You see how Capitan Monastario has oppressed us. My friend Don Ignacio is in prison. Yet you do not seem to care! Do you realize we can no longer stand this tyranny?"

"But father—there's still the law—"

"Monastario is the law!"

"Then we must admit defeat. What else can we do?" Diego asked hopelessly.

"We can fight! We can drive him from Los Angeles by force—"

With frantic gestures Diego signaled his father to be silent. "Please, father—someone may hear you! Don't even mention force. There must be another way."

Don Alejandro sighed. "I cannot believe these are the words of my own son. I had hoped you would grow to be more than a poet and a dreamer."

"I'm sorry, father—"

"It isn't your fault, I suppose. A man cannot help what he is. But you must be tired after your long trip. Go to your room. We shall talk more tomorrow."

In his room, Diego watched Bernardo unpacking the trunks. "My father thinks me a weakling, and it hurts because he is unhappy."

Bernardo nodded and went on working.

"I must fight this Comandante alone, without endangering the lives of any of the *rancheros*," Diego said.

He opened his trunk, pushed aside a layer of books and took out a flat-brimmed black hat, a black cape and mask, and black gauntlets with the letter "Z" emblazoned on the cuffs in silver. In a moment he had donned

the clothes and buckled a sword around his waist.

Bernardo gasped as he saw the black-clad, masked figure before him. Diego grinned.

"May I present myself, Bernardo, as Zorro, the Fox?" he said, bowing low. He drew the sword from its scabbard, and with its point

he slashed the letter "Z" on the inside of the trunk lid. "There!" he cried. "The mark of Zorro! The sign of freedom!"

Suddenly both men stiffened as they heard the drumming hoofbeats of a horse in full gallop. They dashed to the window. The horseman was Don Alejandro, and already he was outside the gates of the *rancho*.

Diego gripped Bernardo's arm. "He's going to try and rescue Don Ignacio! Come on, Bernardo! Zorro rides tonight!"

Bernardo made the letter "Z" in the air and hissed like a sword blade swishing through the air.

"Hurry to the stable and saddle a good horse for yourself," Diego ordered. "I'll be there in a little while."

Bernardo made signs to show that he would also saddle a horse for Diego.

"No. Just for yourself. Now, go," Diego said. Bernardo hurried out, shaking his head and frowning.

When he had gone, Diego stepped to the fireplace and touched a certain brick. There was a grating sound, and the fireplace swung outward to reveal a small room. Diego went in, and the fireplace swung shut behind him.

A saddle and bridle hung on a peg. Quickly Diego took the saddle. Then he pushed against a panel. It slid open, and Diego stepped through the opening and walked down a flight of steps. The panel silently closed behind him. . . .

THE SECRET PASSAGE

Down and down went Diego, and at last he came to a narrow, dark tunnel that widened out into a cave. No one but Diego knew about this place.

A hundred years or so earlier, when the De la Vega *hacienda* was built, the tunnel had been designed as an escape route from Indian attacks. But as time passed it had been forgotten by everyone. One day, Diego accidentally discovered the brick that controlled the fireplace in his room. After that he often explored the tunnel and the cave—but he kept his discovery a secret.

Now, as Zorro, he was making good use of

the passage. He stepped from the cave into the gully, whose rocky sides formed a large, natural corral. Shrilly he whistled, three times.

For a moment there was silence. Then there was the whinny of a horse. Hoofs clattered on the rocks and a great black stallion came into view. He stopped before Diego, rearing and neighing in delight.

"Down, Tornado," Diego said, patting the horse. The animal grew calm and stood quietly as his master saddled him swiftly and noiselessly.

The horse, too, was a secret of Diego's. Tornado had been the leader of a wild pony herd. It was Diego who had caught and trained him. Now, Tornado still roamed the gully and the land beyond. But even after three years he still answered his master's signal, for he had been trained well.

Diego mounted his horse and dashed from the hidden gully. Bernardo was waiting for him at the *hacienda* stable. The mute pointed to Tornado, his eyebrows raised questioningly.

Diego only grinned and said, "I'll explain later. We must go now. And don't forget— when I'm in this costume I'm no longer Diego de la Vega. I am Zorro, the Fox! And now to Los Angeles!"

They reached the main gate of the town, and paused there.

"I'm going over the wall, Bernardo, and this is what I want you to do," Zorro whispered.

Bernardo listened carefully. He nodded, wheeled his horse and galloped to the far end of the stockade that surrounded the town. Zorro uncoiled the lariat from the pommel of his saddle. Standing upright, he twirled and tossed the rope. It looped through the air and the noose tightened on a stake of the palisade.

"Wait for me here, Tornado," Zorro whispered.

Using the lariat as a brace, Zorro climbed

the wall. Then he dropped soundlessly to the parapet and crouched in the shadows, his hand on his sword hilt.

Suddenly a fire bell sounded. This was the signal that Zorro had been waiting for. As the Lancers dashed out from the barracks, Zorro untied the horses that stood outside the building. Frightened by the clanging firebell, the horses stampeded.

Swiftly Zorro made his way to the guardhouse, under cover of the uproar. Sergeant Garcia stood in the doorway trying to make himself heard above the din. Some of the Lancers were chasing the horses. Others had picked up water buckets and were looking for the fire.

Zorro came behind Garcia, pressed his sword point to the Sergeant's back and said, "Step inside, or I'll run you through."

Garcia's eyes bulged with fear. His knees shook so that he barely managed to get into the guardhouse orderly room. Zorro pushed the man into a chair and tied him up with his own sword belt.

Then he gagged him and took Garcia's keys. "Tell Capitan Monastario that Don Ignacio has been set free by Zorro, the Fox! Remember the name—Zorro!"

In the cell block, Zorro found Don Ignacio's cell and unlocked it.

"Who are you?" the old man asked.

"I'm known as Zorro. But there's no time for talking. We must go at once!"

Outside, as Zorro and Don Ignacio ran for the wall, Capitan Monastario spotted them. "Stop them! Stop them!" he cried, drawing a pistol.

But before he could take aim, a squad of Lancers dashed across the Plaza, cutting off his view of Zorro and Don Ignacio.

Zorro slashed out with his sword and the Lancers fell back. He helped Don Ignacio over the wall and vaulted it himself. At the top of the wall he paused long enough to slash a huge "Z" in the wood—the mark of Zorro.

Tornado was waiting on the other side of the wall. Zorro boosted Don Ignacio into the saddle, leaped on after him, and the horse galloped off.

The Comandante flew into a fury when he heard Sergeant Garcia's story.

"Find Zorro! Find him, do you hear? I'll see him hanged!"

He ordered Garcia to take out a detachment and capture Zorro. Then he strode into a small room behind his quarters. A man, trussed hand and foot, was sitting in a corner. Monastario lit a candle and shone the light on the prisoner's face. He grinned with satisfaction. It was quite a feather in his cap to boast of so distinguished a prisoner—a prisoner that he had had bound like a common thief.

"Don Ignacio has escaped—but you will serve just as well, Don Alejandro," he said. "Unless the *rancheros* obey me, I'll order you publicly flogged."

If he intended to make the prisoner plead for mercy, he failed, for Don Alejandro only glared contemptuously at the Comandante.

THE COMANDANTE'S VISIT

When he saw there was no pursuit, Zorro slowed Tornado to a walk. Don Ignacio turned to him.

"Who are you, Zorro?" he asked.

"Perhaps some day I can tell you. But for now it is better that you know me only as Zorro."

"As you wish," said the *ranchero*. "Where are you taking me?"

"To the Mission. You'll be safe there. Father Felipe will give you sanctuary," Zorro said.

"But it is cowardly to hide like that!" Don Ignacio protested.

"You won't be in hiding for long," Zorro said. "You must go to Monterey and tell the Governor what is happening here. He'll send help at once when he learns about the Comandante and his plans."

When they came to the Mission, Zorro and Don Ignacio were greeted by Father Felipe.

"You will be safe with me, Don Ignacio," the priest said, when he had listened to Zorro. "In a day or two, our supply wagons leave for Monterey. You will ride in one of them."

"But the Comandante has ordered all vehicles searched," Don Ignacio said.

"Not even he dares to halt a Mission wag-

on. You shall reach Monterey safely, Don Ignacio, I promise," said Father Felipe.

"Now, it is time for me to leave," said
Zorro. And with a swish of his black cloak
he was gone.

Up in the hills, he met Bernardo at a pre-
arranged place. "You did well, my friend,"
Zorro said. "The fire bells threw them into
such confusion that I was able to rescue Don
Ignacio."

Bernardo grinned with pleasure. "Now we
must hurry back, before we are missed,"
Zorro said.

With Bernardo following, he led the way
to the secret gully, where they unsaddled the
horses and turned them loose.

Zorro guided the wondering Bernardo
through the tunnel to the room behind the
fireplace. There, he took off his Zorro disguise and hung the hat, mask, cape and
gloves on a peg, ready for immediate use.

He showed Bernardo how to work the fireplace control and, moments later, they were
in Diego's room.

"I hope that father has come home," he
said. He knocked on the door of his father's
room, but there was no reply. The room was
empty.

Diego's brow creased with worry. "Bernardo! I can't find him! I'm going out to
search for him. You wait here!"

But before Diego could leave, a trumpet
sounded and a troop of Lancers, led by Capitan Monastario, clattered into the courtyard.
At his signal the men dismounted and stood
by their horses, as the Comandante strode
over to the *hacienda*.

Diego and Bernardo watched from the
balcony. "I wonder why he's here," murmured Diego.

He left the room and hurried down the
stairs.

"*Buenas dias*, Comandante," Diego said
pleasantly. "May I offer you some
refreshment?"

"This is not a social call, señor," said
Monastario coldly. "I'm here to tell you that
your father, Don Alejandro de la Vega, has
been placed under arrest—"

"My father? Under arrest?" gasped Diego.

"He was arrested on the high road by my
patrol—for breaking the curfew," the Comandante went on.

"Surely you don't consider that a serious
offense, Capitan Monastario. What is the
fine? I'll pay it at once."

"Violating the curfew is a major offense—
with a severe penalty," Monastario said.

"I can't believe that—"

"You had better believe it, señor. Your

father is liable to be publicly flogged as one of the state's dangerous enemies!"

"No! You would not dare!" cried Diego in genuine alarm.

"I shall order him flogged unless you do as I say!"

"I shall do anything you say," said Diego, his lips tightening.

"Now you're behaving sensibly," said Monastario. "You will go to the *rancheros* and tell them that unless they co-operate with me, your father will be punished!"

"At once, Comandante!"

"And also tell them neither Don Ignacio nor his family can expect mercy!"

"*Si*, Comandante!"

"And tell them anyone caught helping the outlaw called Zorro will be shot without trial!"

"I am your servant, Comandante!" Diego said, bowing low.

"See that you obey me to the letter. Now, I'm going to Don Ignacio's *rancho* to arrest his wife and daughter. The traitor will find out what it means to defy me."

The Comandante strode out, his sabre clanking in its scabbard.

Diego went to the desk, found paper and pen and hastily wrote a note. Then he called Bernardo.

ZORRO RIDES AGAIN

"Bring this note to Señora Torres," he said. "It tells her to take her daughter and go with you to Father Felipe at the Mission. You must get to the *rancho* before the Comandante. Use the river road—it's a short cut."

The mute hurried off, and Diego sped up the stairs, two at a time. It was the work of a moment to don his Zorro costume and make his way to the gully.

He dug his spurs into Tornado's side, and they galloped like the wind along the *Camino Real*—the King's Highway.

The Lancer detachment was jogging at a slow pace towards the Torres *rancho*. It could already be seen in the distance.

"Now, Tornado!" said Zorro. He rode out in full view of the approaching Lancers. "Cowards! Fools!" he cried, waving his hat. "I, Zorro, call you this!"

Monastario flushed with anger. "Zorro! Get him, men! Get him!"

The Lancers raced for the masked rider.

Zorro held his ground until the steel-

tipped lances almost touched him. At the last moment, he jerked the reins lightly and Tornado sidestepped the onrushing Lancers. Unable to check their charge, they swept by the masked rider. Another tug on the reins sent Tornado up the slope to the top of the ridge that ran parallel to the *Camino Real*.

"Idiots! After him! After him!" screamed Monastario.

Zorro headed for the woods. When he reached the shelter of the trees he slowed down. He soon found what he was looking for—a low-hanging branch. Zorro hauled himself into the crotch of a tree, and at a signal from his master, Tornado darted into the underbrush.

Shouting and waving their sabres, the Comandante and his men came pounding down the trail.

In the tree near Zorro was a hornet's nest. Zorro gave a sly grin as a plan came to his mind. He waited until the troop was almost directly beneath him. Then, with the point of his sword, he pushed the nest out of the tree. It hit the ground in front of the Comandante and burst, loosing a swarm of angry hornets around the Lancers.

The soldiers spurred their horses on with cries of pain, trying to escape the buzzing hornet cloud. From his perch in the tree Zorro watched with amusement as the Lancers leaped from their horses and plunged into a stream, ducking under the water to escape the hornets.

Quietly Zorro whistled, and Tornado trotted from his hiding place. Zorro dropped from the tree into the saddle.

"Our real task starts now, Tornado," he whispered softly to the horse. "We must rescue my father!"

A DARING RESCUE

At a place near the Mission Zorro met Bernardo.

"Are the Torres women with Father Felipe?" he asked.

Bernardo nodded. His fingers moved quickly in sign language and gave Zorro a message that he followed with interest.

"That's good news, Bernardo. The women are safe and Don Ignacio is on his way to Monterey in the Mission wagon train?" Bernardo nodded. "Now, I must rescue my fa-

ther before Monastario has a chance to harm him," Zorro said.

The men headed towards Los Angeles at top speed.

They found the town in a state of excitement. Clanging bells and rolling drums were bringing the people to the Plaza. A stake had been set up, and tied to it by his wrists was Don Alejandro.

Monastario, protected by a cordon of Lancers, addressed the crowd. His uniform was muddy, his face swollen from hornet stings.

"Zorro has interfered with me for the

last time!" he shouted. "As a warning, I'm going to show you what awaits those who defy me!"

He glared at Don Alejandro. "When the sun drops behind the orange grove yonder, Sergeant Garcia will give Don Alejandro twenty lashes with the bull whip he is holding. Do you understand, Sergeant?"

Garcia, standing beside the prisoner, nodded unhappily.

A murmur went up from the crowd, but the people fell silent when Monastario raised his hand.

"But that is not all! Unless Zorro surrenders by sunset tomorrow, Don Alejandro will die before a firing squad!" said the Comandante.

Shouts of protest went up. Some men in the crowd tried to break through the cordon of Lancers, but they were beaten back by the guards.

Slowly the sun went down behind the orange grove trees.

Monastario's voice cut into the silence.

"Sergeant Garcia! Do your duty!" he cried.

Garcia raised his whip. A gasp came from the crowd. Don Alejandro braced for the lash of the whip—but the blow never fell. There was a shout, and a masked horseman charged full tilt towards the ring of Lancers. It was Zorro! The soldiers leveled their steel-tipped lances, but with a mighty leap Tornado vaulted over their heads.

Zorro's sword slashed the upraised whip in half. Another flick of the blade severed the ropes that held Don Alejandro. Zorro swept the old man into his saddle.

Before the Lancers could rally, the masked man and Don Alejandro were away in a cloud of dust.

"After him! To horse, Lancers!" Monastario shouted. But he knew there was no chance of overtaking the masked man on the horse that ran like the wind.

Zorro took Don Alejandro to the secret cave in the hidden canyon.

"Nobody knows this place," he said. "You will find food here, and fresh water. I'll come back when I can."

"*Gracias,* Zorro," Don Alejandro said. He looked searchingly at the masked man, as if trying to see his features. His eyes filled with tears.

"Why are you so sad, Don Alejandro?" Zorro said.

"I cannot help it, Zorro. In you I see the man I wanted my son to be. Who are you?"

"I am sorry, but my identity must remain secret," Zorro said quietly.

"Whoever you are, señor, I am grateful. If only—if only your were my son! Your father must be proud of you."

Zorro lowered his eyes so as not to see his father's unhappiness. "I must go now, Don Alejandro! *Adios!*" he said.

"*Adios,* Zorro!" Don Alejandro said as the masked man galloped away.

Zorro joined Bernardo, and together they laughed about Monastario's anger, and the rescue of Don Alejandro.

Suddenly, Bernardo stopped laughing and sniffed the air. Grasping Zorro's sleeve, he pointed towards the Torres *rancho*. A pillar of smoke was darkening the sky. . . .

ACTION!

Flames were flickering skywards. The men raced towards the smoke. As they drew near,

one of Don Ignacio's *vaqueros* came running towards them.

He recognized Zorro. "Thank heaven you're here!" he gasped.

"Who did this? Who started the fires?" Zorro asked.

"Monastario and his men. He knows Señora Torres and her daughter are at the Mission. He's on his way there now," moaned the man. "He said he'd teach Father Felipe to help traitors; he sent Garcia with a troop to arrest all the *rancheros* in the district!"

"I'll see that Monastario doesn't reach the Mission. Come on, Bernardo!" said Zorro.

Along the dusty highway marched a column of men. They walked slowly, for they were hobbled to each other. Guarding them was a small troop of mounted Lancers.

"The *rancheros!*" said Zorro, his face clouding. "Bernardo, we're going to free those men."

He unsheathed his sword, and charged the Lancers. Behind him came his faithful servant. The sudden attack knocked three Lancers from their saddles, and they sprawled

unconscious on the ground. The rest fled in panic.

Between them, Zorro and Bernardo freed the *rancheros*.

"You are free!" said Zorro, as he loosed the last band. The men thanked him warmly, and left with new hope.

Zorro picked up a cape and hat from one of the fallen soldiers. He removed his disguise and handed it to Bernardo. Then he wrapped himself in the Lancer's cloak and put the hat on his head. Briefly, he told Bernardo his plan. Then he rode off in pursuit of Capitan Monastario.

He soon caught up with the Comandante and his troop. Safe from recognition in his Lancer uniform, Zorro saluted the Comandante.

"What is it?" Monastario snapped.

"Comandante! I have word from Sergeant Garcia!" the Lancer said.

"Well?"

"Sergeant Garcia has captured Zorro! He sent me to lead you to the place where he's holding the prisoner!" said Diego.

"Ah, that's good news!" the Comandante said. He turned to his men. "I'm off to join Sergeant Garcia. Stay here until I return."

Monastario rode off with Zorro, and the weary troopers hitched their horses to a tree and lounged in the tall grass.

After they had been riding a while, Zorro turned onto a narrow trail in the woods and beckoned the Comandante to follow him. Suddenly a lariat snaked from a tree and yanked Monastario from his saddle. He dropped heavily to the ground, and lay there, stunned by the fall.

Zorro grinned as a man jumped down from the tree. "Good work, Bernardo," he said. "Now, let me have my costume."

Bernardo handed him the hat, mask, cape and gloves. Zorro glanced down at Monastario. "He had quite a fall—but it's nothing compared to the one I'm planning for him. Bernardo—his men are camped on the highway about three miles from here. If you stampede their horses there won't be a Lancer in Los Angeles when I get there!"

Bernardo left, and Zorro knelt beside the unconscious Comandante. He took Monastario's pistols, but left him his sword. Presently the Comandante groaned and stirred. He opened his eyes and stared at Zorro in amazement.

"Zorro!" he gasped, sitting up.

"*Si*, Comandante—Zorro! You're my prisoner. . . ."

TRIAL BY STEEL

"Your prisoner! But my Lancer told me—"

"You mustn't believe everything you hear. I was that Lancer!" Zorro said.

Monastario licked his dry lips. "What are you going to do?" he said.

"You'll find out, soon enough. Stand up!" Zorro said sharply.

The Comandante rose. He eyed Zorro nervously. "Zorro, must we fight each other? There's enough in this district for both of us. Can't we—er—make some kind of arrangement?" he said.

"Get on your horse, and don't try any tricks," said Zorro. He tapped a pistol butt with his finger. "I'm a crack shot."

Monastario mounted his horse, and Zorro leaped into Tornado's saddle. He pointed down the trail. "That way. And don't forget, I'll be right behind you!"

Monastario turned to face his captor. "Zorro! That's the way to Los Angeles. I— I don't understand. My Lancers will capture you!"

"I don't think so. They have their own troubles!" Zorro said. He laughed heartily, and Monastario stared at him with a growing sense of fear. . . .

They reached Los Angeles, and Zorro led his prisoner to the church. Zorro rang the great bell, and people ran from their houses, some carrying pine torches. As Zorro pushed Monastario into the flickering light, shouts came from the townsmen.

"Look! Zorro, the Fox, has captured the Comandante!"

"Viva Zorro! Viva!"

"Death to Monastario!"

There was a surge towards Zorro and his prisoner, but the movement stopped as the masked man raised his hand.

"The Comandante is my prisoner! I know he has wronged you—but I mean to see that he gets a fair chance!"

Monastario gestured towards the people. "A fair chance," he sneered. "What kind of chance will they give me—or you, for that matter!"

"Is it true that you're a first-rate swordsman?" Zorro said.

"The best in California—"

"Let's see if that is true! Your sword will give you the chance you want!" Zorro said.

"You challenge me to a duel?" said the Comandante, in disbelief.

"Yes! If you win—Zorro, the Fox, will trouble you no more! If I win—"

"There's no need to say any more," Monastario interrupted. "From this moment, my sword speaks for me!" In one swift motion, he whipped out his sword. "On guard, Zorro!"

Zorro's sabre flashed in the torchlight. A hush fell over the crowd and the only sound in the Plaza was the clash of steel as the men crossed swords.

The duel between Zorro and Capitan Monastario was a grim one. The men circled each other warily. Time and again, they locked blades and came close, hilt against hilt, straining and pushing against each other.

"I'll kill you!" Monastario hissed as they came close to each other.

Zorro laughed. "Threats aren't deeds, Co-mandante!" he said, and broke free.

As the fight went on, Monastario grew desperate. His best efforts had been turned aside by the masked man.

Suddenly he bent low, scooped up a hand-ful of dirt and hurled it into Zorro's eyes. For a moment the masked man was blinded, and the Comandante leaped in to take his advantage. But Zorro, moving with a superb instinct, side-stepped and avoided the Co-mandante's rush.

The crowd grew tense and excited. They knew that this was a life and death struggle. The see-saw battle continued, the advantage going first to one and then to the other. Sud-denly Zorro feinted Monastario out of posi-tion and with a hard downstroke knocked the Comandante's sword from his hand.

The townspeople shouted with joy.

"Zorro! Zorro!" they screamed.

Monastario stood in silent defeat, Zorro's sword point against his tunic. "Go ahead and

finish me off, Zorro. You won," the Co-mandante said.

"I'll give you a chance to live—on my terms," Zorro said.

"What are they?"

"You shall be arrested by a citizen's committee appointed by me, and held until Don Ignacio Torres comes back from Monterey. Then you shall be tried for your crimes against the people," Zorro said.

"I have but one request—" Monastario said. "Let me be tried in Monterey—not here in Los Angeles, where I am hated!"

"Granted," Zorro said. The people cheered themselves hoarse as he turned Monastario over to a citizen's committee. His work completed, Zorro rode away, his cape fluttering in the wind. . . .

ADIOS, ZORRO

A week later, Don Alejandro, his old friend, Don Ignacio, and his son, Diego, were in the *sala* of his *hacienda*. Bernardo served the men wine as they talked.

"What a wonderful week this has been," Don Alejandro said. "The Governor has appointed you, Don Ignacio, as administrator of the district—"

"*Si*. Monastario is to stand trial before a court martial in Monterey—and the Lancers have been disbanded. What more could we ask?" Don Ignacio said. He lifted his wine glass. "A toast, *amigos!* To Zorro!"

"To Zorro!" Don Alejandro said enthusiastically. Only Diego did not drink.

"Come, my son, drink!" Don Alejandro said.

"Frankly, father, I'm bored with Zorro! That's all I've been hearing this past week—Zorro, Zorro, Zorro. . . ."

"Perhaps if you were more like him, I would speak of you," Don Alejandro said. "Where were you when Zorro was risking

his neck for us? I'll tell you! Up in your room, scribbling silly poems!"

"Now, now, Don Alejandro—don't be too harsh on the boy! The world needs poets, too. Everyone can't be like Zorro," Don Ignacio said soothingly.

Neither of the two men saw the amused glances exchanged between Diego and Bernardo.

"Ah, if only I could see Zorro once again —but he seems to have disappeared," Don Alejandro said.

"I wonder about him, too," Don Ignacio said. "But I suppose that now we shall never know. Come, Don Alejandro, don't be angry at Diego. Remember you're holding a gay *fiesta* in a few days."

"As always, you're right," Don Alejandro said. He smiled at Diego and embraced him. "Now, my son—my poet—ride out to the *ranchos*. Invite all the *rancheros* and their families to our *fiesta*."

"*Si*, father. I'll go now." As he left the room he made a slight gesture to Bernardo. The mute waited a few seconds and then hurried from the *sala*.

Diego was waiting for him in his room. "I'm going to let them see Zorro again," he said. "Help me into the disguise. And come with me to saddle Tornado."

He opened a large trunk and took out his Zorro costume. It had been carefully laid away for future use. Then he and Bernardo left the room by the secret passage.

Don Alejandro was about to send for Bernardo for more wine when the servant knocked at the door.

"What is it, Bernardo?" asked Don Alejandro.

The mute signalled frantically and pointed to the window. There was a clatter of hoofbeats in the courtyard, and Don Alejandro rushed over to the balcony.

"Old friend, come quickly! Come quickly!" he cried to Don Ignacio.

There in the courtyard was Zorro, astride his great horse.

"*Saludos, amigos!* If ever you need me again, I'll come to you! *Adios!*" With a wave of his gloved hand and a flutter of his black cape, he was gone.

Don Alejandro stood watching until all he could see was a cloud of dust in the distance.

Don Ignacio smiled gently at his friend, and led him from the window.

"Come, *amigo*," he said. "Zorro may come again, and he may not. He is a brave man, a fighter, and we shall see him only in times of trouble."

"I wonder who he is, and what he does in times of peace?" mused Don Alejandro, almost to himself.

"We may never know," replied Don Ignacio. "But remember, old friend—to be brave, it is not necessary to wear a black

cape and mask. A man can be brave in the everyday clothes that we all must wear, day in, day out."

"What do you mean?" said Don Alejandro.

"Just this. It is always brave to do what one believes in, even if—*especially* if—what one believes in is writing poetry!"

"Yes, yes, you are right," said Don Alejandro. He sipped slowly at his wine. "One thing is certain, though. No man can be both poet and fighter."

"Very few men," said Don Ignacio. "After all—who knows? Perhaps Zorro writes poetry in his spare time!" He clapped Don Alejandro on the shoulder, and the two men laughed heartily.

"Oh, oh! Zorro writing poetry! That is a good joke, my friend!" said Don Alejandro, wiping his eyes.

Behind them stood Bernardo, and he, too, was smiling at the joke.

THE COLD-BLOODED
PENGUIN

WAY DOWN at the bottom of the world near the South Pole, where the summers are even colder than the winters, there lived a little penguin. His name was Pablo.

Now Pablo wasn't like other penguins.

All the other penguins spent their time out of doors. Day after day, no matter how cold it was, they would go fishing, skiing, or tobogganing, in the ice and snow.

But Pablo stayed in his little igloo and huddled close to his warmest companion, an old wood stove called Smokey Joe.

Pablo was unhappy. He shivered and shook as the chills ran right through him. He turned first one side to the stove and then the other.

"Br-r-r-r-r!" he said, through chattering teeth. "I j-just c-can't g-get w-warm.

"If only the sun would come out and thaw all this old ice and snow. Then green grass would grow at the South Pole, and flowers and trees would spring up and life would really be worth living! But that's impossible," sighed poor Pablo.

So Pablo threw more wood into Smokey Joe and huddled closer to it.

Suddenly a bright idea struck him. If the warm weather wouldn't come to Pablo then Pablo would go to it! He would strike out for some tropical island where there were palm trees and coconuts, and where he could spend the rest of his life basking in the warm sun and gazing up at the blue sky overhead.

So the determined little penguin buckled on his snowshoes, said good-bye to Smokey Joe, and bravely set forth for the isle of his dreams.

All his friends turned out to see him off.

They were very fond of Pablo, even if he was cold-blooded, and they hated to see him go, but Pablo had made up his mind. Nothing was going to stop him.

Out over the deep snow the little penguin plodded, towards the north and sunshine.

But he hadn't gone very far from his igloo when a blast of cold air struck him and froze him stiff as a board. He toppled over backwards and rolled down the steep hill. As Pablo rolled, the snow stuck to him until he was wrapped up in a huge snowball.

Faster and faster the snowball rolled down the hill, and bigger and bigger it grew, until it crashed right through the door of Pablo's igloo. It broke open in the middle of the floor.

Pablo sat up and found himself staring at Smokey Joe, who had been burning faithfully, trying as hard as he could to keep the igloo warm.

"Now perhaps you'll give up this wild idea," grumbled the old stove, "and stay where you belong."

But he didn't know Pablo. The little penguin was not going to let one disappointment upset his plans.

The next day the cold-blooded little penguin set out once more for tropical sunshine.

This time he took precautions against his feet slipping on the frozen snow. He tied a hot water bottle to each foot and strapped several more around his waist to keep him warm.

"Now," he cried triumphantly, "I can't fail!"

Pablo started up the hill again.

"Ah, this is more like it," he smiled to himself as the hot water bottles on his feet

got a good grip on the snow. He stopped
and pulled out a map. "Before I go any
farther," he said, "I'll just make sure I'm
going in the right direction. Hmm, let me
see. If I keep going north I should reach the
bottom of South America."

Then a sad thing happened. While Pablo
stood there on the snow-covered ice trying
to read his map, the hot water bottles under
his feet melted their way down through the
snow and ice.

Luckily for Pablo some other penguins
came by just as he disappeared through the
hole in the ice.

Back to his igloo they carried him, frozen
solid in an enormous block of ice. They set
the block on top of Smokey Joe and stoked
him up with wood.

Slowly the ice melted and little Pablo
jumped down to the floor. Apart from being
a little colder than usual, he was none the
worse for his experience.

For a long time after that the cold-
blooded penguin did nothing. He just sat in
front of Smokey Joe and fed him firewood all
day long.

The other penguins were convinced that
Pablo had at last given up his silly idea of
trying to find a tropical isle.

But not Pablo. Oh, no. He was thinking.

"There must be some way to get away
from the South Pole," he thought. All of a
sudden he jumped up and ran out of his igloo. "I've got it!" he cried excitedly. "Of
course. Why didn't I think of it before? I'll
build a boat!"

Working feverishly, Pablo sawed a big
chunk out of the ice in the shape of a boat.
Then he fitted it with a mast and a sail and
took aboard all the things he thought he'd
need on his long voyage—food, water, a
chart, an umbrella in case it rained, a bathtub, and, of course, his old friend Smokey
Joe.

Finally the cold-blooded little penguin set sail for the land of his dreams.

Day after day the cold wind blew up from the south and carried the little ice boat farther and farther north.

As he got nearer to Cape Horn, a blanket of fog rolled in. Pablo had no idea fog could be so thick.

Then one day when the fog lifted suddenly Pablo saw land quite close on the port side. Then more land loomed up on the starboard side. Pablo was puzzled. How could an ocean have two opposite coastlines so close together? But when he looked at his chart he saw the reason. He was sailing through the Straits of Magellan.

"So far so good," thought Pablo as he steered his boat in between the rocky little islands that were dotted about. "This is really adventure."

He sailed safely through the Straits, then turned north up along the cliff-lined coast of Chile.

After Pablo had been at sea for many days the wind dropped and the sail flapped idly against the mast. Pablo was worried. He knew that without a wind to blow the boat along he would just drift about there in the middle of the ocean. And his water supply was running low.

Then one morning a little storm cloud came up. It was only a baby cloud, but it was better than nothing. Closer and closer it came until it hovered right over the boat.

"If it would only break," thought Pablo. "It's probably full of rainwater."

The little black cloud came lower and lower and bumped into the top of the mast. Pablo held up his umbrella open as the little cloud burst open. But all that came out was a single drop of rain.

"Oh, well," sighed Pablo, "it tried hard. Maybe it was too young to leave its mother."

Just as Pablo was almost giving up hope of ever reaching land, once again a breeze sprang up. It filled the sail and drove the ice boat hard on its northerly course along the shores of Peru.

"Why, I'll soon cross the equator," said Pablo, looking at his chart, "whatever that is."

But that wasn't so easy, as Pablo soon found out. He didn't know that the equator was the line that stretched all the way around the middle of the world to divide the southern half from the northern half. And he didn't know that he had to get special permission from Father Neptune himself before he could go across.

So Pablo sailed right into it and bounced back so hard that the little ice boat nearly capsized.

Father Neptune bobbed up from the ocean to see what was the matter. Pablo explained that it was an accident, and that he was just a cold-blooded penguin looking for a warm tropical island with blue skies and flowers.

"Glad to help you out, son," said the old King of the Sea after he had introduced himself. "I know just the place. Turn left right here and follow the curl of the waves until you hit the Galapagos. They're as pretty a group of tropical islands as you could wish to see."

"Thank you, sir," said Pablo.

Then Father Neptune lifted up the line with one hand and Pablo sailed his boat right under it.

The warm tropical sun beat down on the little boat as Pablo lay stretched out on the deck, enjoying every minute of it. This was better than freezing at the South Pole. He dozed happily, completely forgetting that his boat was made of ice. The warm currents

melted it away so fast that by the time Pablo awakened there was very little left of the little boat.

The little penguin ran frantically back and forth trying to save his ship. But it was too late. The only thing that remained afloat was the bathtub. Pablo struck out for it with all his might and reached it just as it was filling with water. Scrambling inside, he bailed it out as fast as he could. But the faster he bailed the water out the faster the bathtub seemed to fill up. Then he remembered he had forgotten to put the stopper in the tub. It must have gone down with the ship.

Something had to be done. Pablo pulled off the shower pipe and jammed it into the hole in the bottom of the tub. The water spurted up through the shower pipe and poured out over the side. As it did so it pushed the bathtub through the water at a terrific speed.

Straight towards a smooth sandy shore sped the tub and slid up on the beach.

Pablo jumped out excitedly. He scooped up handfuls of the fine white sand and let it run through his fingers.

"At last!" he cried. "I'm on a tropical island!"

There were coconuts as big as footballs hanging in clusters from the tall trees, big bunches of yellow bananas, luscious persimmons, ripe juicy mangos. In fact there was everything his heart had ever desired. This was truly the isle of his dreams.

And so the cold-blooded little penguin built himself a hammock and swung it between two palm trees.

And all he did each day was to bask in the tropical sunshine and eat fruit and drink coconut milk.

Pablo should have been the happiest penguin in the world. But there were times, as he lay in his swaying hammock, basking in the sunshine, when he would sigh, long and deeply.

He was thinking of the crisp cold, the gleaming snow, and the clear green ice of his old home at the far-off South Pole.